OUR STORY

of

ATLANTIS

or

THE THREE STEPS

with preface by

EMERSON M. CLYMER

and

with introduction by

DR. PAUL P. RICCHIO

•

Published by

BEVERLY HALL CORPORATION

QUAKERTOWN, PA.

PREFACE

In presenting this revised edition of OUR STORY OF ATLANTIS we are, first of all, complying with the requests of many students and the reading public for the re-issue of this book. Secondly, we have tried to make it more interesting, more valuable and to relate it to later history.

It must be remembered that the original work was written at a time when there was much speculation and many theories on Atlantis and its history. In order to avoid controversy, it was necessary to avoid contradicting accepted theories. This resulted in what may appear to be discrepancies, but this is unimportant since the main purpose of the book was to present an Arcane novel that would receive wide acceptance by the general public and, at the same time, serve as a text for the sincere student seeking interpretations of Divine Law. In this, the author was eminently successful in that OUR STORY OF ATLANTIS is one of the most widely read authentic novels revealing Divine Law.

We will not comment on the conclusions arrived at as to the origin of Man. We are not concerned with Anthropology but with the Spiritual nature of Man. Thus it is not until Man was given a Soul that our interest begins.

We hope that the reader will find this an interesting edition of a great novel and receive a great deal of enjoyment in the reading and study. Our greater hope is that he will find it a source of new Light in his search for The Way.

"Beverly Hall"
October 1972

EMERSON M. CLYMER
Supreme Grand Master: *The Æth Priesthood*
The Fraternitatis Rosae Crucis

INTRODUCTION

OUR STORY OF ATLANTIS, OR, THE THREE STEPS

In the compilation of THE THREE STEPS we have endeavored to provide in one volume three outstanding works insofar as their importance to the AUGUST FRATERNITY and THE GREAT WORK are concerned.

This is not without ultimate benefit to the seeker, the student of the Occult, as it brings to mind and INNER CONSCIOUSNESS those glorious eras that have been, and that CAN BE ONCE MORE.

The purpose of the compilation is to permit the sincere reader to see himself or herself in this life according to the intention of THE DIVINE PLANS and not as an irrelevant speck of human dust. It is our hope that the reader become imbued and inspired with the awesome possibilities of man's spiritual potential, as depicted in OUR STORY OF ATLANTIS.

In the First Step, as Dr. Phelon vividly brought to light, the reader learns that the happenings in his life are not the result of mere chance; they are predicated on the obedience or dis-obedience to the inexorable DIVINE LAWS which govern all things. These LAWS are certain and unfailing and will never lead you astray, because "AS YOUR PAST Made Your Present, SO YOUR PRESENT THOUGHTS, DESIRES, AND DEEDS Will Make Your Future".

As the pendulum of time has begun its return once again out of the darkness of man's ignorance and inertia into the light, there is in this troubled generation an increasing desire for truth — a desire that can be fulfilled only by comprehending the LAW OF REINCARNATION as it continually operates in unfoldment and development which is disclosed before the eyes and understanding of the sincere reader.

Whereas in the past, the LAW OF REINCARNATION may have been a stumbling block or an obstacle to one's acceptance of truth, it now becomes THE KEY which unlocks the mysterious doors of age and time. As presented herein, man has at once *A Reason For Being* in this world where every man can so think, act, and live that he may gain the optimal advantages in each lifetime, LIFTING himself up to those heights from which he would desire to BEGIN ANEW in the next successive lifetime.

What is given in this manuscript of the history of one of the most advanced nations and peoples of all times is not alone important, but *what is* given that we *too*, may advance and progress in harmony with the LAW, is vital to the sincere seeker.

The First Step shows how man has within his grasp an unlimited possibility to advance and raise himself on every plane of being that he can desire. No longer can there be a place for the failure, the weakling, or the drone in society for the CAUSE of one's position will at once be seen and fully recognized in the eyes of THE LAW.

The Atlantians, and Egyptians which followed, utilized the doctrine of REINCARNATION to the full, DESIGNING AND PLANNING WHILE STILL IN THE FLESH for the NEXT INCARNATION that which they wanted to be SPIRITUALLY, PHYSICALLY, AND MENTALLY, sanctioned to the full extent by THE DIVINE LAW which they OBEYED.

By unquestioned OBEDIENCE to THE LAW which governed and guided their everyday lives, the Atlantians witnessed the perfection of THE LAW as manifested in the building of their cities, their government, education, and conduct of matters material and spiritual. To the LAW they looked for the planning of all things as a natural function of their being.

OUR STORY OF ATLANTIS portrays the just and rightful respect for womanhood and her most sacred place in the family as she dedicated herself to her productiveness as a woman, seeking not to avoid the divine responsibility of her marriage.

All things were conducive to the growth and perpetuation of one's family with proper perspective given to MAN, WOMAN, AND CHILD as Divine Law would have it. That sickness and disease were *unknown* would be difficult for today's nations and peoples to understand, as they know not the experience or benefits of fulfilling DIVINE LAW, having been overshadowed so long by disease, the REaction of disobedience to THE LAWS.

As is revealed, the INSTRUCTION and GUIDANCE of the student, the seeker of Occult Mastership, has not changed throughout the centuries. In Secret Schools then, as now, development of the DIVINE was only possible by INDIVIDUAL Guidance and Instruction and was not broadcast in a classroom as was education in academic subjects.

The magnitude of willful compliance with Divine Law was evidenced in Atlantis to the extent that enlightened man was permitted to control the weather, the oceans and seas, and natural elements in accord with Divine Law. The Atlantians understood that GOD does not dwell in the darkness of ignorance and superstition. Their GOD was our GOD OF LIFE, who permitted man to utilize ALL THINGS PROPERLY, to control the elements when necessary, or to travel through the infinite spaces to any or all planets he was able to reach. As the most Venerable Magi taught Neophytes then, and centuries later, nothing is denied man except that which he has not earned or of which he is not worthy.

Being in full accord with the supplications of the Priesthood Councils of forty-five, fifteen, seven, five, and the Exalted Third, how could ATLANTIS have been otherwise than the closest to HEAVEN ON EARTH ever achieved?

In the Second Step, THE FUTURE RULERS OF AMERICA dwells on the recurrent dominant theme of the preceding work. Herein are set forth experiences of a Master Initiate intricately involved with the dim but glorious past of ATLANTIS.

Once again, distinct positive reference is given to a highly SPIRITUALLY ADVANCED and developed people who made OBEDIENCE to DIVINE LAWS their dedication — dedication to obedience in the complete TRUST OF THE LAW in preparation for their COMING ROLE in the Drama of the Heavens incumbent upon the people of America.

As can be readily understood by reading between the lines, these people are "imprisoned", that is, they have CHOSEN THEMSELVES in preparation for the Armageddon through which America is destined to pass in keeping with the ancient prophecy. Having already entered a new cycle of time. "The New Age," the time is not far off, in keeping with the prophecy contained in The Future Rulers of America. That this process is well under way is clearly shown within the shadows that the coming events have cast before them. We see daily the increase in the number of WOMEN who seek guidance and instruction in the DIVINE WAY, the NATURAL WAY. They have already formed the circle of the SELF-DEDICATED, GLORIFIED MOTHERS-TO-BE through their desires to prepare bodies for these returning souls, THE COMING MASTERS, thus having accepted the DIVINE LAW as their guide in affairs of life.

The Third Step, THE BROTHERHOOD OF THE ROSY CROSS, presents the true mission of AMERICA, "THE LAND OVERSHADOWED WITH WINGS," the PROMISED LAND, where enlightened man may continue his struggle to KNOW GOD!

Down through the ages the August Fraternity has continued to function under many climes and under many names, always with purpose and intent that the FIRES be kept burning in the Temples on the mount or in the caverns, LIGHTING THE WAY for those yet to come.

As the destiny written by man's own hand on the walls of time began to unfold in the minds and hearts of stalwart men, THE LEADERS began to arrive on this new continent. To fulfill this great promise — THAT THE LAW MIGHT FUNCTION — they arrived from the EAST and from the WEST taking their places among men.

Known only to each other as THE BROTHERHOOD OF THE ROSY CROSS they watched zealously the birth of this new nation, a "babe" among wolves, that no possible harm could come to it.

Imbued WITHIN AND WITHOUT with the burning SPIRIT OF FREEDOM for mankind, they set about with no thought of self, family, or possessions to manifest on this NEW LAND, LIFE, LIBERTY, AND THE PURSUIT OF HAPPINESS as a GOD-GIVEN RIGHT.

"THE BROTHERHOOD OF THE ROSY CROSS" by the Master Initiate George Lippard further demonstrates the theme of ATLANTIS and The Future Rulers of America as no more and no less than the "Reaping" of that which had been "Sowed."

As you have been drawn to read this volume, feel yourself BECOME A PART OF AMERICA, relive this most timely and Soul-stirring message by George Lippard, REVEALING and UNFOLDING the most glorious privilege of being an AMERICAN! You will see your destiny disclosed in the moving drama of American History as the story of WASHINGTON, his Spiritual Ordination as the LEADER IN THE DESTINY OF AMERICA, unfolds before your eyes.

THIS IS YOUR HISTORY, YOUR AMERICA, The New Nation Overshadowed with Wings, conceived long ago in the HEARTS AND SOULS OF Great Men, destined to be the mightiest in all the world under the guidance of dedicated men FULFILLING DIVINE LAW. This then, IS YOUR BOOK . . . it is for you who LOVE AMERICA and who continue in determined DEDICATION TO MAKE YOUR OWN AND HER FINAL DESTINY AN ACCOMPLISHED REALITY!

Dr. Paul P. Ricchio
July 7, 1972

OUR STORY

of

ATLANTIS

Written down for the

HERMETIC BROTHERHOOD

and

THE FUTURE RULERS

of

AMERICA

By

W. P. Phelon, M.D.

and

Together with a Biography and
Extensive Notes

By

R. Swinburne Clymer, M. D.

Published by

BEVERLY HALL CORPORATION

Quakertown, Pa.

BIOGRAPHY

D<small>R. W. P. PHELON</small> was graduated as a Doctor of Medicine in the year 1869 from the College of Physicians and Surgeons, Keokuk, Iowa.

This college was organized in 1849. Four years after its organization it became the Medical Department of the University of Iowa, at Keokuk, and, upon the organization of the Medical Department of the State University of Iowa at Iowa City, in 1870, the original name was assumed. In 1899 it consolidated with the Keokuk Medical College of Keokuk, Iowa, forming the Keokuk Medical College, College of Physicians and Surgeons. In 1909 it merged into the Drake University, College of Medicine.

While still in college, Dr. Phelon became acquainted with the works of Dr. Paschal Beverly Randolph, the Rosicrucian, and thoroughly imbued with the philosophy as taught by the Fraternity of which Dr. Randolph was Supreme Grand Master at the time. However, it appears that Dr. Phelon's mind was of a Mystic rather than an Occult trend, and deeply interested in Hermetic Science, and in 1871 Dr. Randolph introduced Dr. Phelon to his Egyptian associate, the *Orthman Asward el Kindee*, then attaché of the khedive of Egypt.

Some years later, possibly about 1879, the exact year being unknown, Dr. Phelon visited Egypt and was there introduced into the Hermetic Brotherhood of Atlantis, Luxor and El-phante and through this connection first became an Initiate of the Triple Temples and later was accredited with the original Charter which the Egyptian Initiates affirmed had been received from the Atlantian Lodge by their ancient brethren, and with full authority to establish the Hermetic Brotherhood in America.

Shortly after his return to America he and Mrs. Phelon, herself a physician, established a practice on Fulton Street, Chicago, Ill., and later removed to Jackson Boulevard, Chicago, where they remained until they moved to San Francisco, Calif. Shortly after establishing their practice they formed the Hermetic Grand Body of America, and Knot Number One, The Hermetic Brotherhood of Atlantis, Luxor and Elphante, was instituted there.

Besides his *Temple Talks,* which were issued beginning with the institution of the Brotherhood and continued until his death, which occurred in San Francisco, Calif., his best-known books are: *Future Rulers of America,* 1887; *Hermetic Teachings,* 1889; *Three Sevens,* an invaluable Occult novel upon the theme of which practically all Occult novels of later days are based, 1889; *Mysteries of the Sphinx and Pyramids,* a study made while in Egypt; *Witch of the Nineteenth Century,* 1893, and *The Story of Atlantis,* published in 1903 after the Phelons had moved to that city and there established the Hermetic headquarters.

Dr. Phelon remained active as a teacher and the Supreme head of the Hermetic Brotherhood until his transition to spiritual Atlantis, which took place at the good old age of ninety-five.

In 1908 all authority possessed by the Hermetic Brotherhood of Atlantis, Luxor and Elphante was transferred to the *Confederation of Initiates,* of which it remains an active part.

OUR STORY OF ATLANTIS

CHAPTER I

THE LOST ATLANTIS

Fair Atlantis, peerless country!
Lulled within the Ocean's arms,
Lying beautiful and shining
Far beneath the storm's alarms;
Never has a plague come near thee;
In thy halls were love and ease;
Now, above thee, lost Atlantis!
Roll the ever-restless seas.

In those histories, half tradition,
With their mythical thread of gold,
We shall find the name and story
Of thy cities, fair and old;
Dreaming bard has told in fancy,
Wandering minstrel sung of thee,
Now, above thee, lost Atlantis,
Rolls the ever-restless sea.

Every heart has such a country;
Some Atlantis loved, and lost—
Where upon the gleaming sand bars
Once life's fitful ocean tost;
Mighty cities rose in splendor;
Love was monarch of that clime;
Now, above that lost Atlantis,
Rolls the restless sea of Time.

Happy he who, looking backward
From a life of larger scope,
Deems a youthful, idle fancy
His lost continent of Hope;

Or, by light of love and gladness,
Finds the present home sublime,
Glad that over his Atlantis
Rolls the restless sea of Time.

Why is this book written? is the most pertinent question asked an author at the outset of composition. It is echoed and re-echoed by critic and reader upon its publication. It certainly appears to be a fair question whenever the subjects seem so much out of the routine of ordinary information as the present volume.

The scattered records of the Past, within the historical period, would apparently yield scarcely enough material to make a short magazine article of any interest, to say nothing of swelling in size to the dignity of a book.

It is now conceded, however, by our wisest scientists, that every configuration and corresponding circumstance points to the possibility of the existence of an island-continent in the neighborhood, if not directly over the great West Indian Archipelago, just as the whole configuration of the North American Continent tells the story of the inland sea that broke through its barriers at the Thousand Islands in the St. Lawrence River and, hurling itself over Niagara Falls, left the habitable valley of the Mississippi as a legacy to man for future settlement.

The sacred writings of all nations concur in the same declaration and statement of disaster to some portion of the earth, most generally including all. In a late issue of *Mind* appears an article headed: "A Monument to Atlantis," which says: "A notable discovery of more than ordinary interest for historians, especially those who have a leaning toward antiquities, has lately been made by the well-known archæologist, Augustus Le Plongeon. This discovery should particularly attract the attention of Americans, since it enables them to lay claim to one of the most important monuments of ancient times. The edifice in question is the Pyramid of Xochicalo, standing 5396 feet above the level of the sea, and situated to the south-southwest of Cuernavaca, sixty miles from the City of Mexico. For more than a century the pyramid has been occasionally visited by distinguished travelers, including the learned Humboldt; but none succeeded in discovering the purpose for which the monument had been erected, nor in deciphering the mysterious inscriptions on its side.

As far back as 1886, Dr. Le Plongeon published his alphabetical key to the Maya hieroglyphics, comparing this with the ancient Egyptian hieratic alphabet. He has now found that the signs on the Pyramid of Xochicalo are both Maya and Egyptian; and a careful study of these decorative inscriptions has made it plain to him that the pyramid was a monumental structure erected to commemorate the submergence and destruction of the great Land of Mu (Plato's Atlantis), together with its population of 64,000,000 of human beings, about 11,500 years ago.

Dr. Le Plongeon, in his remarkable work, "Queen Moo and the Egyptian Sphinx," gives four Maya accounts of the same cataclysm. This, then, is the fifth, and, in his own opinion, the most important of all the known records in Maya language of the appalling event that gave rise to the story of a universal deluge that is found in the sacred books of the Jews, the Christians and the Mohammedans.

These records, on stone, on sun-dried bricks, on papyrus, all tell the same story. The little we know of the Aztecs is also confirmatory of the same fact. Whence came the people of South America, with their advanced civilization and traditions of the past? What mighty people built the great cities and temples of the now forest-covered cities of Yucatan and Central America, with their carved glyphs, and correspondencies to the hieroglyphs of the Valley of the Nile and the East Indian entablatures, and, moreover, on almost precisely similar styles of architecture to those of Egypt and India? Is it reasonable to suppose there was no common bond of fellowship between all these? The Ancient Egyptian ideas have dominated the world down to the present day. Instead of a mummy-case, we use a coffin for our dead. The idea is the same—the departed ghost was to be saved the trouble of making a new body, perhaps at short notice, at the great day of the resurrection.

The trinity in unity of God, now universally received, was an Egyptian idea, and the same is wrought into the stone tablets which Le Plongeon and his amiable wife have unearthed in the forests of the Maias and Quiches.

If the nation, of which these are but the feeble remnants, had not disappeared by some cataclysmal climax, we must certainly have had some later historical data. As the mind of the present generation is more largely than ever desirous of Truth, the idea of Astral presentation and perception may not be without its weight, especially as the books of Wisdom of the Past declare that automatic books of record are kept of all deeds and manifestation upon the earth.

It may be asked why those who have entered into the rest of the Unseen should be at all concerned in the unfoldment and development of the race who are ever toiling over the rocky paths of the planet. If the doctrine of reincarnation is true, then would it not be to the interest of the coming Egos for all the race of men to be advanced just as far as possible, so that the reincarnated from time to time might receive the highest advantage attainable from their touch with the earth at any particular time? Those who are coming back into the present civilization, if they were of the advanced and cultured classes of Atlantis and the most ancient Egypt, would find more advantages of acquirement, through our leisure and experience, than when hurled into life amid the horrors and darkness of the Stone Age.

From time to time, the material and data obtained, as hereinafter described, from which this book is made, have been pressed upon my attention as something that would be of use and interest to all who are seeking to KNOW. I do not doubt the authenticity of my information nor the statements given as facts by those who were so kind and courteous as to make the writer their mouthpiece in this recollection of the ancient memories.

I do not doubt that to many readers will come fleeting glimpses of these scenes, as if they had been part of them. It is a conceded fact there have never been, since the fall of Atlantis, so many reincarnated Atlantians upon the earth at the same time as now. This accounts for the almost universal demand out of the Astral records for the forgotten knowledge of the Occult which they there recorded. This also explains the readiness of the public mind to receive knowledge of the doctrines of Mental Healing, Spiritualism, Theosophy and Occultism in all its branches.

Ignatius Donnelly finds a supporter of his Atlantis theory in Sir Daniel Wilson, president of the University of Toronto, who declares after a great deal of search that the lost Atlantis was not a myth, but that it was really a part of the continent of America. He accounts for its disappearance from view in a different way, but that is merely incidental.

Donnelly's theory was that the land was submerged by some great volcanic upheaval and that from those who escaped to the continents of Europe and Asia came the tradition of the deluge. Sir Daniel rejects this explanation as being disproved by the fact that there are no traces of such volcanic action either on the continent or in the ocean bed. He believes that the ancient Egyptians, the most progressive and adventurous people of ancient times, discovered the continent, but that in the decline both of their learning and power it became lost to view and existed at the time our knowledge of Egypt begins merely as a shadowy tradition.

It is his opinion that traces of the Egyptians of those days are to be sought in the ruined cities of Central America, whose origin has never been determined nor even been made the basis of any reasonable theory. Such a discovery would furnish a substantial basis for the legend of the lost Atlantis, and the theory invests those wonderful ruins with a new interest for the antiquarians.

The St. Louis *Republic* said: "Atlantis was a continent supposed to have existed at a very early period in the Atlantic Ocean, over against the Pillars of Hercules," but which was subsequently sunk in a cataclysm of which history gives no record. Plato is the first who gives an account of it, and he is said to have obtained his information from some Egyptian priests with whom he had come in contact. Plato's account says: "Atlantis was a continent larger than Asia and Africa put together, and that at its western extremity were islands which afforded easy passage to a large continent lying still beyond— this last-mentioned continent being now supposed to be South America." Nine thousand years before the time of Plato, according to the tradition, Atlantis was a powerful, thickly settled country which extended its way over Africa and the major portion of what is now Europe, "even to as far as the Tyrrhenian Sea." Further progress of the invasion of the Atlantides was checked by the combined efforts of the Athenians and other Greeks. Shortly after the invaders were driven from the continents of Europe and Africa, a great earthquake shook Atlantis from center to circumference. First, the outlying islands sank; then great areas of the mainland. Waves ran mountain high across hundreds of square miles of what had the day before been fertile fields. Great temples were racked and riven, and the affrighted populace climbed upon the ruins to escape the encroaching waters. On the second day, after a night of terrors which no pen could possibly describe, the earthquake shocks were of greatly increased violence, ending only after the entire continent had been engulfed. There is no page in history or tradition that records a more frightful catastrophe, and nothing would be of more absorbing interest than a work entirely devoted to giving an account of what is known concerning it.

To the objector who urges that the explorers of the world have never discovered any traces of the great city and continent whose story I have endeavored to give in the following pages, permit me to give a few straws floating on our sea of current literature which show that the history of past ages may yet be read in the central part of our continent:

"The recent report that a citizen of the United States has discovered among the mountains of the Mexican State of Sinaloa a long-forgotten city tallies with a curious local tradition of the region. Adjoining the State of Sinaloa on the south is the State of Jallisco, and of this State Guadalajara is the capital. Living in the mountains of Jallisco, part of the great Sierra Madre or "Mother Range" that extends through Sinaloa and thence northward, are the unconquered Yaquis, a brown-haired people with light eyes and almost fair complexions. Guadalajara is the only civilized town that these Yaquis visit, and it has long been believed there that the Yaqui fastnesses of the Sierra Madre range conceal not only rich mines of silver, but as well the lost city of the Aztec race. No one has hitherto pierced the mountain wilderness, because the naked Yaquis have an effective system of passive resistance that has hitherto successfully closed the sole line of approach. The only human beings other than the Yaquis themselves admitted to the mountains of Jallisco are a few renegade Apaches, murderous wretches, vastly more dangerous to would-be explorers than the peaceful but persistent Yaquis."

There is no question in the minds of those who have given attention to the subject that the Aztecs are the lineal descendants of the mighty nation who sought to know beyond the law governing the created. Of the unknown city above mentioned, we add another description from a different source:

"During the frequent visits I have made to Mexico," said a mining engineer of Philadelphia to an *Inquirer* reporter, "I have come in contact with many of the Indians resident there and have heard some very singular stories. One which all the Indians unite in telling is that far in the interior exists an enormous city, never yet visited by white men. It is described as peopled by a race similar to the ancient Aztecs, who are sun worshippers and offer human sacrifices to their deity.

"The race is said to be in a high state of civilization, and the Indians say that the city is full of huge structures which are miracles of quaint but beautiful architecture and are situated on broad, paved streets, far surpassing those of the City of Mexico.

"One Indian, I recollect, assured me that he had seen the city and its inhabitants with his own eyes, but had been afraid of being captured and had fled. Of course, I did not believe him, but, all the same, it is not a little strange that the accounts of the Mexican Indians relative to the mysterious and magnificent interior city agree perfectly."

These are but few of the many allusions and traditions pointing to the fact that somewhere in the Southwest there is a people who undoubtedly hold a complete historical record of the chain of events from Atlantis in its prime down to the present day. While there is perhaps but a single city inhabited and secluded from the outside world of today as keepers of the Ancient Wisdom, we yet find ruins of such magnitude as to impress us more strongly with the idea that the people who builded the original structures could not have wholly disappeared from this continent. The following, from San Diego, Calif., we offer in proof, calling attention to the fact that the dragon is a favorite design in the East Indian sculptures:

"The ruins of a prehistoric city have just been discovered

by a party of prospectors from Yuma when on the Colorado desert in search of the Pegleg mine. The wind had laid bare the walls and the remains of the stone buildings a distance of 420 feet in length by 260 feet in width. Gigantic pillars, quaintly carved to represent dragons' heads and rattlesnakes, still stood in the sands of the desert, supporting on their tops huge slabs of granite weighing many tons. The frieze ornamentation resembled Egyptian sculptures and exhibited a greater degree of skill than is possessed by the Indian artisans of the present day. Fragments of pottery were found underneath the debris and, together with the crumbled piece of frieze, were brought by one of the party to this city. One of his associates came to San Diego, and the others returned to Yuma nearly two weeks ago. But the story of their discovery was carefully guarded, in the hope that in some way they might profit by it.

"The discoverers, in company with four others, afterward went to the desert to explore the ruins. They were driven back by a sandstorm, reaching this city today, but will make a careful examination of the ruins in the season when the conditions are favorable for extensive explorations. From the relics exhibited it is evident that an important archæological discovery has been made."

In connection with the above, there is a peculiarity to be noticed in the occurrence of the sandstorm. It has always been so. A storm or some sudden natural event has warded off all efforts to reach these wonderful remains of the prehistoric or even the existing cities. When men shall be ready to seek them, desiring knowledge and not treasure, there is no doubt the keys for the unlocking of the mysteries of the past will be given into worthy hands, and what we have herein written will receive ample corroboration. We add still another account of wonderful discovery in proof of the immense population of the old Atlantian kingdom in its prime. This time it is from the City of Mexico, the center of the modern Atlantian or Aztec civilization:

"What appears to be the verification of an old Aztec fable of a buried race of cave-dwellers and a hidden city in south-western Mexico is a matter in which the local scientists are interested at present. L. P. Leroyal, a French engineer, who has lived long in this republic, has just arrived from the wilds of the Southwest and reported that he has discovered in the State of Guerrero a huge natural cave, which he believes to be the greatest in Mexico, if not in the world. He says it is much larger than the famous cavern of Cacahuamilpa, situated some distance south of Guernavaca, which has hitherto been supposed to be the largest natural cave in existence in Mexico. Mr. Leroyal, after penetrating a considerable distance into the cave, determined to make a thorough investigation of it and, accordingly, a few days ago furnished himself with food sufficient for a day, provided himself with lanterns, etc., and set out upon his task all alone. As he went along he made a thorough plan of the cave, but did not anticipate that his task would be as arduous as it proved. At the first the bottom of the cave was a gradual slope downward, then changed upward and afterward alternated for the most part between descents and ascents. Here and there, however, a level bottom of great width was met. The height of the cave varied, as might naturally be expected; in some places it was several hundred feet high. For some distance from the entrance no trace of human beings was found. Occasionally magnificent stalactites and stalagmites, the finest Mr. Leroyal had ever seen, were met.

"After proceeding for some hours he came upon what had evidently been an ancient cemetery, as there were at least 400 petrified bodies, together with ancient idols, etc. There was also a fountain of beautiful, clear spring water, which was found to be excellent. Some of the tools, as well as two or three skulls, Mr. Leroyal brought away with him, and they are now in this city. The appearance of this charnel house thus lighted up for the first time in hundreds of years was gruesome in the extreme and well calculated to shake the nerves of the explorer. Mr. Leroyal continued his explorations while hour after hour passed. It was not until after he had traveled a distance of at least twenty-one and one-half leagues that he thought it time to call a halt and proceed on his return journey. So far as he could see, the distance still to be traversed might be very considerable, with the chances for the cave opening out, as the floor seemed to be well trodden by human feet. He retraced his steps as speedily as possible and, after being underground for upward of twenty-four hours, found himself once more at the entrance of the cave. Mr. Leroyal promised to make further explorations before long. It is expected that a party fully equipped for the exploration of this wonderful cavern of the dead will soon be fitted out under the guidance of the discoverer, and the outcome of the investigations will be awaited with interest. The natives of the locality, as, in fact, the Indian population in general in Mexico, believe that at some place near the southwestern coast of Mexico there exists a great white city with countless treasures which has never been seen by white men, the approach to which is so intricate and cleverly concealed that a stranger has never entered its solitary precincts."

With all the increasing mass of information on the subject, it seems there should be some effort at collection under guidance of what is known about Atlantis the Mighty. To make a beginning and thus call attention in this direction is my answer to the question: "Why is this book written?"

ATLANTIAN MEMORIES

Out of the dim Past, old memories come to me,
From where the light in all its glory seemed to be,
As the people worshipped near the Sun's resplendent rays
And, lotus-crowned, hailed with joy the festal days.

Golden lyres, sending forth rich, harmonious strains
Sounding the keynote which o'er the world still reigned.
High above all, the Vestal's song enchanting soars,
Mingling with the ripples on the wave-washed shores.
From the Temple floats the bell's melodious chimes,
So deep and mellow in that old Atlantian time.

Throughout the Ages linger these old memories still
And hover 'round me with no effort of my will.
Still in my heart is throbbing with the rhythm of the waves,
Those slumbering waves which, alas, became our graves.
Again I hear the glad hosannas to the Sun arise.
Isis in the sanctuary is veiled from human eyes,
Which read no warning in the skies' celestial hue;
Nor heard it murmured in the Ocean calm and blue;
Neither listened to the whispering wind so free,
Telling of the doom fair Atlantis was to see.

I am thankful that the gates of memory ope,
That great Angels weave the scattered threads of hope
And clothe us freshly with its robes of snowy white,
While on our altar shines again the mystic light;
The radiant star which once o'er Egypt shone
Glimmers once again with a message all its own.
Humble tho' the Temple, the melody is there;
The bell's sweet chiming breaks upon the silent air;
Amid the incense arising from our sacred Shrine,
Old Atlantian glories round our spirits twine.

CHAPTER II

THERE is yet a little more of the flotsam and jetsam upon the stormy waves of human unfoldment which is supplemental to our opening chapter and must be detailed now or put entirely to one side. From two distinct sources we give an account of an old Mexican city that has never been entered by the foot of a white man and which was known to be in existence long before the Spanish Conquest:

"Mr. Juan Alvarez, who has just returned from an exploring expedition in the southwestern part of the republic, reports that he has found a city which has never been entered by a white man and which has evidently been in existence for hundreds of years, going back before the time of the conquest of the country by the Spaniards. It is an old Aztec city, and the approaches to it are so guarded by nature that it is an impossibility to reach it if the inhabitants do not want a traveler to get in.

"The city lies in the almost inaccessible mountains in the extreme southwestern part of the country and is so far away from civilization that few white men have ever been in the neighborhood. It was by the purest accident that Alvarez became aware that a city was anywhere in the vicinity, and after he found it all of his endeavors to reach it were unavailing on account of the persistent opposition of the natives.

"He had been traveling over the mountains in search of an outlet to the Pacific Ocean when he came to the top of an elevated plateau and crossed to the farther edge. He had a magnificent view, and while looking over the country saw what he took to be houses in a far-distant valley. A close inspection with a glass convinced him that what he saw was really a col-

lection of houses, and he at once set about reaching the place
to see who lived in that part of the country.

"After days of hard work, climbing over cliffs and mountains,
he reached a point from which he obtained a good view of the
city and saw that it was regularly laid out in streets and was
peopled with a race who knew something about civilization.
The houses were of stone and were surrounded by yards in
which were growing flowers and shrubs. On all sides were evi-
dences of taste shown by the inhabitants, and it was evident
that he had found a city which was not known to the outside
world.

"A careful examination of the country showed him that the
city was located within a natural amphitheater and was accessible from one side only. He saw that the only means of access
was through a long and narrow defile which led into the mountains from the Pacific coast side, and he started to reach the
place where he could find this entrance. He made an outline
drawing of the city as it appeared to him from the distant
mountain top, and this is all he has to show that there is a city
within the heart of the mountains, for he was never allowed to
reach the spot.

"From this drawing it is plain that the city has not less than
four thousand inhabitants. The houses are all of stone and are
supplied with doors and windows. In the center was a large
building, which was undoubtedly the temple of worship, for on
its walls could be seen sculptured designs representing the
Deity. It was in the shape of the ancient teocalli, which is to
be found in many parts of this country, and the people could
be seen passing in and out of it during all hours of the day.

"After ten days' arduous work, Alvarez found himself at the
foot of the mountains on the western slope and set about
searching for the canyon leading to the city. He had so well
marked the lay of the land that he had no difficulty in finding

the entrance, but he was met by a band of Indians who refused to let him proceed. They offered him no violence, but insisted that he should return. He told them that he had come over the mountains and did not know how to find his way back.

"After a consultation, he was told he would have to remain awhile as a prisoner, and two runners were sent into the mountains, who returned in a day with orders from someone in authority, and Alvarez was blindfolded and placed on the back of a mule. He traveled in this condition for three days, only having the bandage removed from his eyes at night.

"On the fourth day he was told to remove his bandage, and when he did so he found himself on the borders of the Pacific Ocean. The Indians had gone, leaving him with nothing to guide him back to the place where he had seen the city."*

We conclude our extracts with the description of another mighty city, the work of the powerful nation whose capital, located on the great island of Atlantis, exercised its power both east and west, of which we are trying to tell:

"The American archæologists who went to the recently discovered city in the Sierra Madre Mountains have returned and tell of another hidden city five Spanish leagues north of the first city. The leader of the party, C. W. Pantion, of Philadelphia, says that these cities were evidently twin capitals of a wealthy district long before the Aztecs appeared. The two cities are connected by underground passages hewn out of solid rock, and it was while exploring one of these passages that the second was discovered. It lies in a deep basin of the mountains, with no exit except the underground tunnel. At least none has been found."

To that which we have thus drawn from all accessible sources in the visible, I now desire to add supplementary tes-

---

* This city is described in full in *Future Rulers of America* and has been visited by persons in the body who have been permitted so to do.

timony from the Astral Records, which I believe to be reliable and worthy of credence.

Does not this collated evidence of the similarity in nature and civilization west of the great city, which could not possibly have had commerce with the mother-country for centuries, prove conclusively, even to the realistic and scientific mind, a common origin for religious teachings, customs, languages, both oral and written? All the discoveries relative to this subject confirm this conclusion. We are indebted to those who are impelled by an irresistible desire to learn and know. Who in this cause are willing to expatriate themselves, endure danger and overcome obstructing difficulties, if they may but by some chance guidance bring again to the light of day some of the various records which were left when the sun of the manifested spiritual world went down into the shuddering earth?

To the Aryan people,[1] who listen with a willing heart, there is much that can be given concerning this ancient city. It matters little how Science and Religion shall accept that which is offered, whether in a scientific way or from the unseen, as true and of value. Science and Religion have never received anything new upon untried lines of thought until they have been

---

[1] For the purpose of classification, four distinct peoples will be recognized throughout these notes. The first is a sub-human class conceded to have been the Neanderthal man. We say "sub-human" because this was the creature in the process of formation into the human form as we know man today. While the body had proceeded far in its development, the head and brain had not yet reached that stage where thinking and reasoning were possible. Ages were required to develop this being or creature into what was to be man in the true sense of the term.

The first race bearing the form of man and distinct from all other creatures, that is, having the capacity to *think,* was the dark or black race whom we know as the negro. This race came into existence in Lemuria.

The second race in this classification is that of the yellow or copper race. His place of beginnings is unknown, but in all probability between Yucatan and upper South America.

The third race is that of the Aryan or white race. His place of birth or beginnings was Atlantis.

forced to the exception.

That is why the priests of all ages are so conservative and have withheld so much more than they should, even on their conservative line of thought. It has ever been their rule to hold fast upon that of which they had become possessed; content and satisfied without the trouble and exertion of seeking new fields for themselves or admitting the possibility of broadening truth for others.

All that has ever been learned, to distinguish the savage from civilization, was known to the wise men of Atlantis. Whenever there has been upon the earth a sufficient number of Atlantians at one time to control a nation or to form one by themselves,[2] that nation or epoch has always experienced a most wonderful growth. In the days of the last Egyptian splendor, when it was the school to which the Greeks and Romans resorted for instructions, was the last time noted in history of such a reappearance in sufficient numbers to admit of a national control. From what they did, we have the pyramids, the Temple of Karnac and all the mighty ruins of the Nile and the Euphrates in evidence.

As soon as the Anglo-Saxon-speaking races were sufficiently developed out of savagery, the Atlantians commenced reappearing, startling the whole world ever and anon with their great strides toward wisdom and knowledge as they slowly paved the way by conquest and discovery for the settlement and reoccupation of that which belonged to them and for the utilization of all their old resources under new conditions of added strength and experience. In no other way can we account for the wilting and extermination of the red-skinned usurpers who had neither claim nor strength to maintain title to that into

---

[2] Such a period was during the time when the First Council of the Great Brotherhood was held in Philadelphia and the Constitution of the United States was written, signed and sealed. See *The Brotherhood of the Rosy Cross,* Philosophical Publishing Company, Quakertown, Pa.

which they had strayed by accident during the contemporary absence of the real owners.

Much sympathy has been wasted on the red son of the forest.[3] He has but obeyed the law: Who cannot dominate the resources of the environment must yield title to him who can.[4] How much would our vast storehouses of mineral and agricultural wealth have helped man's unfoldment if they had never been used? The difference between the American Indian and the Anglo-Saxon Atlantian is plain to the dullest intellect.

As the city of Atlantis grew, her population was drawn off into colonies which had deep and abiding influence on the whole of the western continent, but especially centering along the belt in which Atlantis itself was located.

Between the fading away of the last Egyptian civilization and the concealment of the world's records at that time there

---

[3] The man or race of men refusing to develop and grow strong by individual effort and failing in making the necessary provision to protect himself and his rights must expect to be annihilated. *God helps those only who help themselves.* The Eternal Unchangeable Law is: "The conquest and subjugation of the weak, shiftless, unprepared." The "sin" and Karmic reaction is in taking unjust and unfair advantage of others; unnecessary destruction and spoliation of the immature and innocent. An immediate example in this the year of our Lord 1937 is the unholy and unmerciful and "ungentlemanly" destruction of the non-combatants in China. Another was that of the conquest (?) of Ethiopia. These butcheries will bring upon these nations the same manner of retribution as is now being visited upon the Spanish people for the terrible and unspeakable outrages of their forefathers upon the Sun-Children of Mexico and other South American peoples. We Americans are not wholly without Karmic reaction because of our early treatment of the American Indians.

[4] "By the sweat of thy brow shalt thou live" is the fiat which has come down the ages—since the days of Adamic man. This means that though we may become rich in worldly possessions we must nevertheless at all times keep fit and be prepared, *in every respect,* to meet those who would take from us that which we have gained. God gave man the Law: *Be prepared at all times; no man knoweth when the hour cometh.* This is as truly so respecting all things of life as it is of that which we know as *death.* Stand firm, keep fit, be prepared to protect thine own, but take not that which is not thine own, for thy neighbor is thy brother.

is a mysterious gap which can be accounted for only in one way. When Atlantis was in its prime there were other units in the world's category of nations which were not so far advanced. If Atlantis had held on in the even tenor of her way, all other nations of the world would have received the light and been uplifted to something near its own standpoint, but when this chance of development was cut off, they groped in comparative darkness. When this class of people incarnated again in force of numbers such scenes as the conquest of Rome by the Goths and Vandals, the overrunning of Europe by the Huns and the eruption of the Tartars, times without number, occurred. As they disappeared from the mortal vision, we can but recognize their sameness of purpose and the most pertinent fact that undone duty made all this trouble for the Atlantians of the Far Past, their comrades and associates. Have we learned the lesson that no human being is separate from our ourselves? A wrong once done must be righted. It is the eternal law of exact justice.[5]

---

[5] This is as true of the nation as it is of the individual. There is individual Karma just as there is a national Karma. Both *must* be paid— *the Law itself exacts it*. All great nations of which we have record degenerated and were defeated and then enslaved by *less* mentally and spiritually developed nations because they had forgotten their birthright and permitted themselves, through luxurious living and inactivity, to become weak. When Rome and its empires were tenanted by pastoral peoples, laboring long hours, living temperately and keeping brawn and brain fit, they were the rulers of the world. When cities sprang up and the people left the farms to live therein; when hours of labor were shortened and muscles weakened; when money was plentiful and degrading practices were indulged in; when leisure was the rule and indulgences universal, weaknesses set in, men's (including women's) minds became debased, nerves shattered, and soon they were at each other's throats, Brotherhood and national cohesion were forgotten, man was secretly against his fellow, foreign inimical influences were gradually implanted into native minds by paid agents and soon the Holy Roman Empire fell into barbaric hands. *This is the history of all nations.* America, the *land overshadowed with wings*, God-chosen and young as she is, is rapidly falling into the identical errors of which Roman and other nations of the past were guilty. Will she awaken in time? Will enough Atlantians be reborn to save her?

As these misbegotten *impedimenta* to progress pass out into the unseen, having overborne or put off all heads that towered above their own intellectually, Atlantian influence revives. Little by little have these "fellows of ignorance" felt the uplifting of influence of the "sons of light," and every generation increases the widening wave of educated and spiritualized people which must finally include within it every nation, tongue or people of the earth's full complement of inhabitants. The American nation has done a vast deal for the enlightenment of the whole world. Thus it is easy to understand why the extinguishing power of all that holds the soul in chains is projected toward us.

In the ancient times, when the lamp of civilization burned at Rome and Athens, or later, as at Antioch and other cities, single centers of learning blazed out and lessened the darkness as do beacon lights set on a hill. But with these compare the events of today. A compact, unified nationality which resembles the old Atlantis had its beginning on an island cut off from easy approach. Yet it has been able to make its power felt throughout the whole world. Although the English name be detested, its power is always respected. Not only has this nation made itself felt everywhere, but it is the founder of the American nation and unites its force with that to push the common civilization and thought-currents into every part of the globe.

The freedom of the thought-body and the aptitude of the minds engendered thereby have once more drawn to the American continent more Atlantians than were ever incarnated at one time since the fall of that city. It thus happens that their inventions and knowledge and wisdom and the results of thought-force, modified and perfected by the assimilation of hundreds of years in devachanic rest, are coming upon the nation in a flood, as with outstretched hands they demand from the Silence that which they themselves deposited in the Astral Records long ages since.

We often wonder at events transpiring in the way of discoveries or at the applications of principles which are perfectly logical and linked one to another. We have surely reached a point and begun to guess about the uses and methods of application of that vehicle of force about which the Atlantians knew much,[6] and, desiring to know more, found there was a limit which barred their further progress. We already have hold upon another, and we desire only that they who may essay to advance in this direction may do so with body, Soul and mind so purified they will not need the reprimand of obstruction that came to the original investigators of our nation on that line.

The reason why this age is so celebrated above others of the near past is due to the facts thus stated. We perceive in the near future, as has been repeatedly foretold, the end of a cycle is at hand.[7] Cataclysmic results, the sinking of land in some

---

[6] A little more than thirty years have passed since this was written, and all that is implied therein has been made manifest. Alas, it is also true that many of the inimical forces which proved the undoing of other nations are at work here, resting neither night nor day, to destroy the natural cohesion and Brotherhood of Man. Can these destructive forces be retarded and finally eliminated? It is possible, but nothing less than the drastic measure of deporting all alien forces and the elimination of the selfish interests of egomaniacs athirst for power can prevent a national calamity. We are *not* calamity-minded, but we are mindful of the history of many nations of the past, nations which had attained both age and greatness.

[7] We have entered this new Cycle, the New Age, wherein there is a new interpretation and application of the old Laws. In this New Age every man must assume personal responsibility, without the thought of evasion, for all his acts and must accept the fact of a Karmic reaction for all he does. No longer is it possible for man to place the responsibility for his evil actions upon his fellow-man nor upon a world Savior. He alone is guilty and he alone must pay upon his Soul. This is the age of *Manisis,* of a New World Order—the establishment of Brotherhood and the elimination of all retarding forces. *The New Age is upon us.* Either we harmonize with it and its laws or we shall be destroyed by it. Ours is the choice.

places and the rising in others is imminent. When cities peculiarly situated are crowded with inhabitants who have lost all conception of everything but their own desires centering in selfish purpose, their thought vibrations become inharmonious with the universal thought vibrations. If this inharmony continues strong enough to communicate itself to the ground upon which the city stands, this foundation being subject also to a set of vibrations upon the natural plane of Liquidity, serious consequences may occur.

Just what the outcome of the present period will be, none but the Council of the Seven Great Builders know. But this we have gathered: That within a hundred years, and possibly a much shorter time, Atlantis will be above the waves. Whatever her monuments contain or whatever may be in her ruined temple can then be investigated.

Within 500 years the bulk of population will be south of the equator; that which is now sea will become dry land, and the old continent of Lemuria will once more sustain its millions of inhabitants. Scientists tell us that the time is fixed when all the gold, silver and coal will be mined. How short-sighted! Under the sea is a thousandfold more than has ever been brought to light by man's busy hands.

CHAPTER III

IN THE early seventies, having by constant and severe attention to business reached a point when rest and change were
imperative, I was advised by my physician to take a sea voyage. I mentioned this fact to a friend of mine in New York
City who was a vessel owner. He offered me the position of
supercargo in one of his vessels about to sail for San Francisco "around the Horn." I gladly accepted the chance, for it
gave me both motive and occupation for the trip.

My preparations were made rapidly. We sailed out of New
York Harbor on the 15th of June, 1872.

As the last lighthouse sank slowly beneath the waves and the
full moon rose in the heavens, I stood watching the receding
landmarks, little dreaming of the momentous events to happen
as a part of the voyage, nor of the marvelous revealings to
come to my knowledge before I should again touch my foot
upon land. Of all these, the following pages are but a feeble
portrayal. But it is always so in life; we meet and part, come
and go. The consequence of the meeting and the pain of the
parting may be inexpressible in spoken language, but how shall
we know? Who will tell or warn us of the swiftly oncoming
future with its burden of weal or woe?

As our vessel was devoted to freight, we, as I knew, carried
but a single passenger, who by especial favor of the owner had
been permitted to occupy the one spare cabin. The rest of the
space was occupied by the officers of the ship, including myself.
I had been introduced to this man when he had first come on
board, but, being much preconcerned about the business I had
in hand at that moment, I had simply responded with the usual
meaningless phrase of: "Happy to make your acquaintance."

But I remembered afterward an impression of dignity of bearing; of sweetness of real courtesy on his part; and that peculiar, indescribable thrill as we shook hands, which once or twice in a lifetime it may be our good fortune to experience as the lines of our lives cross with those who are essential to our highest and best unfolding.

Standing thus, leaning meditatively over the taffrail, I came back to myself by hearing my name pronounced distinctly in a low, musical voice with just the slightest foreign accent. Looking around, I acknowledged the address, as he went on to say:

"I see you are leaving part of yourself behind you."

"Oh, not a large part," I replied, "but I was thinking about the certainty of parting and the uncertainty of meeting."

"Don't you think that we part forever from our friends only when we have accomplished or finished all that we can do for each other? So long as our work remains undone, we shall certainly meet again."[8]

"Yes," I said, "that may be so, but it is the human uncertainty that saddens."

Looking full at this man, to whom, with his every word, I was most indescribably attracted, I saw a picture, from that

---

[8] Two things bind people together and will draw them to each other if parted. One is Karmic Law and the other is Love. No self-will or man-made mandate is powerful enough to keep apart for any length of time those Karmically bound, and this bond is so strong that even death cannot sever it; so powerful that even though both desired to part they would be impotent to do so until their destinies would be fulfilled. Love, on the other hand, is a bond of attraction, and those who truly love each other will be drawn together again and again as long as that love exists though all the universe attempted to part them. Frequently the question is asked: Will those who have been together in life, as for instance, husband and wife, children and parents, friends and relatives, meet and know each other after death parts them? The answer is simple: If there is a bond of *real* love between them, then nothing on earth or in heaven can keep them apart. They will meet again and the old bond will be resumed. *Love is the law;* it is the one and only eternal law, and no force is strong enough to permanently interfere with its functioning.

time indelibly stamped upon my memory. Tall and almost perfectly proportioned. Eyes black, while in their ordinarily kind expression one might easily imagine their possibilities when honest indignation or righteous anger stirred their depths. Hair and beard white and worn a little longer than custom prescribed. His bearing was majestic in strength, serene in harmony, attractive beyond compare in its unselfish desire for the good of others. With all this there was an impression, in all he said, he could tell very much more, if he only would, about any subject concerning which he might be conversing.

It was such a face as children love and scoundrels hate, containing within itself the pitying tenderness of a mother's love and a father's sustaining watchfulness. In our interview I passed from the outermost border of casual acquaintance to the confident championship of sworn friendship. At this, too, I marveled, for I am slow to receive or offer friendship, but come slowly to the perception of what might be in those who honor me with their good will.

Although we stood some little time longer gazing upon the ocean, as the night and waters met in closer and still closer embrace, we lapsed into silence with that strange feeling of being company for each other, although no word was said, and finally we descended to our respective cabins for the night.

As is usual with the position which I held, my duties during the voyage were almost nominal, making up for this leisure, however, during the receiving or discharging of the cargo or any part. Consequently I had sufficient time to improve the acquaintance so curiously begun. It did not take long to find out that my friend was a zealous, unremitting student, and that while we were familiar with many lines of common interest, there were others in which he was well versed, of which I knew comparatively nothing. He was a very eloquent and instructive talker and readily and gladly answered my questions.

Especially was this true of things in the past, which the present generation has moved on and forgotten, and a peculiarity of his descriptions was that they were given as if personal experiences of his own. Later I knew why, but at the first it seemed that it was done to give more life and movement to the story.

As a child I had always been fascinated with whatever I had chanced upon, either in reading or conversation, which related to Atlantis. But as I grew older, enveloped in the materialistic ideas of the modern schools, I had come to regard the little that was known of that ancient mistress of the seas as largely fabulous, if not wholly unworthy of credence.

After we had been out from port four or five days, as we sat chatting on the quarter-deck, something was said which induced me to ask him the question squarely:

"Do you believe there ever was such a country as Atlantis?"

"Most certainly," was his quiet, decisive answer.

"But do you think it possible that a whole continent could disappear so utterly beneath the waves as that is said to have done, leaving no more trace of its former existence than has been the case with that?"

"And why does this seem impossible to you? Does history know anything of the city that stood under ancient Troy? Who knows who were the builders or what the design of the Pyramids of Egypt? Who can tell of the cities lying stratum upon stratum in the valley of the Nile? In your own country, who can tell anything of the Mound Builders? What does the world know of Palmyra, of Babylon, or of the great cities in the valley of the Euphrates? But for the accessibility of their ruins, they would by this time have been as thoroughly forgotten as Atlantis now is.

"And," here his face softened with an infinite pity, "perhaps within forty years from now we may have another lesson in the opportunity for denying the existence of the past.

"But maybe," he continued, "you would like to hear some of the actual records brought down even to your day, of an event that concerns so intimately every living person now upon our planet."

Upon my eager assent he went into his cabin and soon returned with a small black-letter volume, written after the style of the Far East, upon parchment, from right to left. Opening it, he read in his sweetly modulated tones, translating as he read the following extract:

"Facing the Pillars of Hercules was an island larger than Africa and Europe put together. Beside this main island there were many other smaller ones, so that it was easy to cross from one to another as far as the farther continent. This land was, indeed, a continent, and the sea was the real ocean in comparison to which 'The Sea' of the Greeks was but a bay with a narrow mouth.

"In the Atlantic Island a powerful federation of Kings was formed, who subdued the larger island itself and many of the smaller islands and also parts of the farther continent. They also reduced Africa within the Straits as far as Egypt, and Europe as far as Tyrrhenia. Further aggression, however, was stopped by the heroic action of the then inhabitants of Attica, who, taking the lead of the oppressed States, finally secured liberty to all who dwelt within the Pillars of Hercules. Subsequently, both races were destroyed by mighty cataclysms which brought destruction in a single day and night. The natural features of the Attic land were entirely changed, and the Atlantic Island sank bodily beneath the waves.

"In the center of the Atlantic Island was a fair and beautiful plain. In the center of this plain and nearly six miles from its confines was a low range of hills. Here dwelt for many generations the renowned race of Atlan, from whom the whole island and sea were named Atlantic or Atlantis. The ruling Kings ever handed down the succession of power to their eldest sons, the younger sons going into the priesthood. They were possessed of such wealth as no dynasty ever yet obtained or will easily procure hereafter. This wealth was drawn both from all foreign nations with whom the Atlantians traded and from Atlantis itself, which was especially rich in minerals, and possessed the only known mines of orichalcum in the world, a mineral with most wonderful and inexhaustible properties—a metal which was then second only to gold in its value.

"The country was rich also in timber and pasturage. Moreover, there were vast numbers of elephants, spices, gums and odorous plants of every description; flowers, fruit trees and vegetables of all kinds, and many other luxurious products which this wonderful continent, owing to its beneficent climate, brought forth. These were sacred, beautiful, curious and infinite in number. Nor were the inhabitants content with simply the natural advantages of their glorious country, but also displayed a marvelous industry and skill in engineering and the constructive arts. For in the center of the island they built a royal palace, every succeeding King trying to surpass his predecessor in adorning and adding to the building, so that it struck all beholders with the greatest admiration.

"They cut about the Royal Palace a series of waterways or canals. These were bridged over at intervals, while an immense canal admitted the largest vessels from the sea, giving at once protection as a harbor, and making it more convenient for the transportation of freight to and from the interior. In fashioning their interior streams they left docks cut out of the solid rock where their triremes could land their cargoes.

"The stone used in their building was of three colors, white, black and red, so that many of the buildings presented a gay appearance. Their walls were covered with brass (which they used like plaster), tin and orichalcum, which had a glittering appearance.

"Northeast of the center of the continent stood the great Temple. The interior was covered with silver, except the pediments and pinnacles, which were lined with gold. Within, the roof was a magnificent mosaic of gold, ivory and orichalcum, and all walls, pillars and pavements were covered with orichalcum.

"By a system of aqueducts leading from natural springs of hot and cold water, they had supplies for baths and for the irrigation of their beautiful plantations and gardens.

"The docks were filled with shipping and naval stores of every description known to men at that time. The whole city teemed with a dense population. The main canal and largest harbor were crowded with merchant shipping returned from, or making ready to sail for, all parts of the world. The din and tumult of their commerce continued all day long and the night through as well. Such is a general sketch of their wonderful city.

"Now, as regards the rest of the country, it was very mountainous, with exceedingly precipitous coasts, and the plain surrounding the city was itself environed by a mountain chain broken only at the sea entrance. The plain was smooth and level and of an oblong shape, lying north and south. The mountains were said to be the grandest in the world for their number, size and beauty. The whole country was a constant succession of prosperous and wealthy villages, for there was an abundance of rivers and lakes, meadows and pasturage for all kinds of cattle and quantities of timber. They surrounded this plain with an enormous canal or dike, 101 feet deep, 606 feet broad and 1250 miles in length. By it the water from the mountains was conducted around the whole plain, and while a part flowed out to the sea, the rest was husbanded for irrigation. They were able, by raising two crops a year, to double their productive capacity.

"In the polity of the Atlantians the Kings maintained an autocracy, and the priesthood were their council of consultation in all matters of State, until at last the power passed into the hands of the priesthood.

"For many generations, the rulers, Kings and priests remained obedient to their ancestral traditions, for they possessed true and altogether lofty ideas and exercised mildness and practical wisdom, both in the ordinary vicissitudes of life and in their mutual relations. They looked above everything except virtue. They considered things present of small importance and contentedly bore their weight of riches as a burden. Nor were they intoxicated with luxury, but clearly perceived that wealth and possessions are increased by mutual friendship and the practice of true virtue; whereas, by a too anxious pursuit of riches, the possessions themselves are corrupted, and friendship also perishes therewith.[9] Thus it was they reached the great height of prosperity we have described.

"But when at the last their mortal natures began seeking to dominate and override the Divine within and about them, they commenced to display unbecoming conduct and to degenerate, thus blighting and finally destroying the fairest of their most valuable possessions."

"This," said my friend, "is as authentic an account as that

---

[9] Wealth and possessions are of no value in themselves, since they are of the immediate present and a day hence may be lost. However, as a means toward an end, for use in the general betterment of all, as well as the advancement of self, they are both desirable and necessary. Riches are a responsibility; something either earned or given us for use in the development of all that is beautiful and desirable. The moment we begin to think of worldly possessions as "ours" we take a step downward; it is the beginning of selfishness. Only *two* things are *real*, though they possess no substance. These are Love and friendship. Love is more or less selfish, since it seeks as its own that which it loves. Friendship gives rather than takes and forgives where Love would ignore.

of any nation of whom we have any history, for it was handed down from father to son in the ancient Atlantian writing, which was perfected about 25,000 years before the Christian era commenced."

Just then some duty claimed my immediate attention, and as he rose up to return to his cabin he looked me fully in the face and remarked: "If I mistake not, the time is close at hand when your desire for information on these lines will be more fully gratified."

CHAPTER IV

I T WAS a day or two before we had a chance for any more conversation, for he seemed to be very busy in his own cabin with what looked like an ancient map and a number of diagrams of cabalistic calculations, which I fully recognized, for I had some experience with researches along that line and could, to a certain extent, verify some of the simpler rules of deductions from the Cabala. But, as I could see, the operations upon which he was engaged were very complex and far-reaching and concerned some of the mightiest secrets of planetary creation.

I also noticed, while the problems seemed very abstruse and complicated, he did not seem at a loss in any sense or puzzled, his absorption being the result rather of the length of the process.

At last he appeared to have reached a favorable conclusion, and his data and memoranda were put away. Once more he came upon deck. Although for a few days he apparently put aside a continuation of his former talk about Atlantis, yet there was an uplifted expression of content, lending an added charm to the ever-restful dignity of the perfect face.

While he had been thus busy it had occurred to me I had an odd volume in my locker I had picked up in a second-hand stall in Boston, intending to examine it at my leisure. Now, having my interest aroused, I brought it out and found among much that was quite discursive the following pertinent paragraphs:

"The fourth continent,[10] which it has been agreed to call

---

[10] The first continent, for the purpose of classification, was undoubtedly that unknown and forgotten land where the race of beings who

Atlantis, was formed by the coalescence of many islands and peninsulas that were upheaved in the ordinary course of evolution and became ultimately the true home of the great race known as the Atlantians, a race developed from a nucleus of Northern Lemurians,[11] centered, generally speaking, toward a point of land in what is now the mid-Atlantic Ocean.

"In connection with the continent of Atlantis we should bear in mind that the account which has come down to us through the old Greek writers contains a confusion of statements, some of them referring to the great continent as a whole, and others to the last small island of Poseidonis. Plato, for instance, condensed the whole history of the continent of Atlantis, covering several millions of years into an event he located upon the island of Poseidonis (about as large as Ireland); whereas, the priests spoke always of Atlantis as a continent as large as Europe and Africa put together. Homer speaks of the Atlantes and their island. The Atlantes and the Atlantides of mythology are based upon the Atlantes and Atlantides of history. The story of Atlas gives clearly to us the clue. Atlas is the personification in a single symbol of the combined continents of Lemuria and Atlantis. The poets attribute to Atlas, as to Proteus, a superior wisdom and a universal knowledge and especially

---

ultimately took on human form were in the process of development, possibly the home of what we know as the Neanderthal man; the second continent that of Lemuria; the third continent that which was probably Easter Islands, the home of the first yellow or copper race, and, lastly, the fourth, or Atlantis.

[11] The author is in error. The Atlantian, white or Aryan race, could not possibly have developed from the Lemurian or truly colored race. The pigmentation of the skin alone precludes this possibility. The Lemurian and Atlantian were two distinct races, dating to two distant and distinct periods of time or creations, possibly millions of years apart. Were there any possibility of the Atlantian race having descended or ascended from the truly colored race, then the first race would long since have passed out of existence, one having given way to the other. Such, however, is not the case; the colored or negro race maintains its characteristics today as fully as when history began.

a thorough acquaintance with the depths of the ocean, because
both continents, having borne races instructed by divine masters, were each transferred to the bottom of the seas, where
they now slumber until the appointed time shall come to reappear above the waters. And as both Lemuria, destroyed by
submarine fires, and Atlantis,[12] submerged by the waves, perished in the ocean depths, Atlas is said to have been compelled
to leave the surface of the earth and join his father, Iapetus,
in the depths of Tartarus.

"Atlas, then, personifies a continent in the West, said to
support heaven and earth at once; that is, the feet of the giant
tread the earth, while his shoulders support the sky, an allusion
to the gigantic peaks of the ancient continents, Mount Atlas
and the Teneriffe Peak. These two dwarfed relics of the two
lost continents were thrice as lofty during the day of Lemuria
and twice as high in that of Atlantis. Atlas was an inaccessible
island peak in the days of Lemuria, when the African continent
had not yet been raised.[13]

"Lemuria should no more be confounded with the Atlantis
continent than Europe with America. Both sank and were
drowned with their high civilizations and 'gods,' yet between
the two catastrophes a period of about 700,000 years elapsed.

"Why should not your geologists bear in mind that, under
the continents explored and fathomed by them, in the bowels
of which they have found the Eocene Age, there may be hidden
deep in the unfathomable ocean beds other and far older conti-

---

[12] Lemuria was only in part destroyed. Part of that ancient continent
exists today as Africa, still the home of the true negro. Atlantis, however, was wholly destroyed; Lemuria by fire, Atlantis by water.

[13] An error. It is true that Africa as it is known today did not exist
in the days of Lemuria. We might here use a scale as an illustration.
Lemuria was then an immense land connected with what is now Africa
and jutting into the ocean. As Lemuria sank, that which is now the
continent of Africa arose, that portion near the ocean was the pivot
point, the balance, and the people thereon again peopled the newly
arisen continent.

nents whose strata have never been geologically explored, and that they may some day upset their present theories?"

Amazed at this singular corroboration of what my friend had previously read me, I concluded I would ask him something more about it at the first opportunity, not dreaming that the opportunity of lives was close at hand.

During all this time we had been making good time toward the South. Both officers and men had been attracted toward our passenger, and all were ready to give him the little attentions which make a stranger feel at home anywhere. I mention this as explanatory of some events which happened a little later.

The winds had been brisk and favorable, but as we approached the Spanish Main they grew fitful, and when we had traversed a part of that West Indian Archipelago, they fell away into a dead calm. Our ship drifted a little to the South, but made no particular headway. On the third day the moon fulled at noon, and we were lying in about 30 degrees North latitude and 42 degrees West longitude, when my friend asked me if I would like to go with him to visit a peculiar-looking island about a couple of miles to the westward. Upon my rather eager assent, the captain granted us the use of his yawl, and though he proffered us the help of some of the crew, our friend declined, saying he had been much accustomed to the water.

We pushed off, I taking a pair of oars and he steering. I had hardly taken a couple of strokes with the oars when I felt that the rapid impulsion of the boat was not due to my strength. I glanced at my companion. His face was set with a peculiar expression, of which I had before had experience in other directions.

A very short time sufficed to bring us to this island, which on closer inspection seemed to be the summit of some huge obelisk or pillar, a little raised above the waves. The sides, although not high, were sheer and precipitous. In the still waters they extended below the surface as far as vision could penetrate. How much farther, I had no means of ascertaining. We rowed slowly around it. It was about 150 feet in circumference. On the side farthest from the vessel the face of the rock was broken jaggedly by the weather. The projections gave opportunity for fastening the yawl and for climbing to the summit. If there had been any swell of the ocean, even this would have been impossible, but with a sea of glass all about us it was not a very difficult task. Having securely knotted the boat's painter to a stout protuberance, we scrambled as best we might to the top.

To my utter surprise, instead of the flat, solid mass, roughened by the weather, which I expected to find, it was cup-shaped in the center, evidently filling with water during storms and drying out under the hot sun. It was now dry at the bottom. Looking closely at the sides, I saw that, instead of being a mass of natural rock, it was a structure built of masonry by cunning hands, so perfectly and solidly as to defy thus far the fierce action of the most erosive forces of nature. The floor was laid in regular flagging. Almost stunned by the discovery, I turned to my companion, but my exclamation of surprise was checked by his actions. Standing erect in the very center, with his face to the North, guiding himself by a small compass and a little square of parchment, upon which characters were inscribed, he turned 15 degrees to the East and stepped forward one pace. Then turning 15 degrees more, he stepped forward another pace. He repeated this operation until he faced due East. There, standing erect, his form seemed to dilate and his face grew fixed and set in its whole outline. All at once I perceived a large disc of stone had revolved at his feet, exposing a flight of stone steps leading into a room below. Coming back to himself, he motioned me to follow him, and slowly we descended the stairs into an ante-room below, opening into a larger room. As we stepped upon this floor a light, which came from nowhere in particular, lighted up the whole interior. Limitless age had laid its desecrating hand upon everything. But as this had been hermetically sealed by the waves, the dust that would otherwise have accumulated in the upper air was not present. In the center of the room were five stone seats; on each was a little pile of dust. My companion, still silent, stepped to the East and, facing the seats, made one of the signs of Power. As he did so I thought I heard a suppressed sob of joy, but it was not distinct enough to be unmistakable. Then, going to the exact opposite side of the wall, which was partitioned into a series of curious entablatures, he touched some mechanism, which, preserved through the ages, obeyed the will of this wonderful man. A door slid back, through which we passed into a chamber below. Here we found seven seats. On each rested those curious little piles of dust. My friend repeated the sign made in the room above, and then a sound like the tremor of an Æolian harp rose in volume until the vibration filling the room shook the walls of the tower in which we were standing. Turning to the Eastern face of the wall, from a niche therein he drew out a little stone box. Holding this carefully, he retraced his steps toward the upper air, closely followed by myself. With the greatest care he closed behind him every avenue, thus sealing once more for future unfolding whatever there might be of knowledge or mystery here concealed. When the disc at the top had rolled into its place a roll of pigment was placed in his hand by unseen helpers. With this he traced upon the tightly joined edges a character which burst into a silvery flame as it appeared upon the stone and left a blood-red mark behind it. Then, proceeding to the side where the boat lay waiting for us, we managed without any difficulty to seat ourselves in it and push off, he steering, as before.

Singular as it may seem, without any preconcerted instruction or word of warning, not a word had been interchanged between us from the moment of our landing until we were again in motion upon the water. On my part the silence was involuntary. I seemed to stand in a vortex of recurring memory, coming down overwhelmingly upon me. I was too busy within myself in attempting to readjust the past, the present and the promises of the future, to leave any time for the frivolity of speech. I could not resist the feeling that these rock-ribbed chambers were in some peculiar way a part of myself. I knew I had been perfectly familiar with the purposes of their erection, their use and of some final issue, appalling and benumbing in its effect. More than that. The five seats of the upper chamber and the seven seats of the lower, to my inner vision, were filled with an occupant, shadowy but so distinct I could recognize the features as one recalls the lineaments of a long-absent friend. Then came the names, as if I had parted with them only yesterday. Oh, Memory the Eternal! was it yesterday or thousands of years ago since I looked upon these faces and forms of comrades loving and true? The feeling of present reality, of some tie stronger than friendship, overwhelmed me. When my friend made the sign I mentioned, a burden of untold weight was lifted from my shoulders, as if an expiation were finished, a terrible mistake rectified whose consequence all my life, up to that hour, had cramped and restrained all my unfolding and its energies. All this and much more that words will utterly fail to portray held me silent as my friend did, what he evidently came to do, taking me as an involuntary accomplice.

Sitting in the stern of the boat, facing me, with the stone casket resting on his knees, he looked at me with a grave smile and said:

"My brother, I see my confidence in thee was not founded **in simple assumption, but in knowledge. Thou hast learned** well the lesson whose closing clause is to keep silent.[14] Thereby thou hast proved also thy position in the Great Brotherhood, whose first charter was issued by the Atlantian Kings. I greet thee, Ancient Wise One."

While saying this his whole face lighted up as if from an inner fire. The action of the sympathetic exaltation on myself was beyond the power of words to describe. It was as if one had suddenly come to a perception of almost infinite power and without a particle of arrogance in the possession. I could only reply:

"I feel that we must have been brothers, but you do me great honor in naming me thus."

"Before we reach the ship I must tell you," continued my comrade, "that it has been permitted you for purpose to re-visit the tower of the Great Temple of Atlantis, in which were gathered for concentration during the last awful cataclysm, which sent the continent beneath the waters, all the living members of the most potent Brotherhood that has ever existed.

"You entered the chambers of the three, the five and the seven.[15] The whole continent is slowly rising once more. The top

---

[14] The *First Great Law*. To Know, to Dare, *but above all,* to keep *Silent*. A simple Law, yet one which appears to be the most difficult for Neophytes to master. Weeks, months and even years pass in training and yet, with it all, Acolytes seem to be unable to comprehend the Law of Silence. They *must* talk. They *must* reveal secret things. They simply must discuss the things they know or *think* they know, forgetting that *he who knows does not talk.* The silent tongue is an unknown posses-sion. When they meet fellow-travelers something compels them to gos-sip, to reveal personal secrets, to discuss their own practices, their own growth; what they know of the intimate life of other students, of their instructor and guide, and all the while they wonder *why* the Door of the Secret Temple is not opened to them, why they are unable to unveil the Seat of the Mystic Flame. *Gabbleism.* It is the weakness of the human race. Vanity, self-righteousness and desire for glorification dic-tate to a weak mouth, and the tongue must wag—and the *Door remains closed to them.*

[15] Today known as the Councils of Three, Seven and Nine. The weak-ness of the Five has been eliminated and the strength of the Seven substituted.

of the tower, which was 100 feet in diameter at the base and 210 feet high, has again reached the upper air. The transparent dome which covered the chamber of the three has been destroyed by the action of the waves. We do not know whether the masonry of the upper stories will be able to resist the erosion of fierce tropical storms or not, as little by little it reaches the surface.

"It was thought best by the Brotherhood to rescue this"— here he touched the little casket—"before it might be overwhelmed and forever hidden by the insatiable maw of the waters. It contains the fullest continuous record of the last years of our once glorious country, at present accessible.

"The chambers which we entered were built perfectly air- and water-tight, and for that reason have preserved their contents to the present time. Below the last chamber we entered was that of the fifteen,[16] and still below that, the chamber of the forty-five. I did not enter them, for I was warned that I might thereby afford opportunity for the waters, pressing up from below, to wipe out all vestiges of this ancient home of the Brotherhood, which to later generations may be ocular demonstration of our existence.

"Obligation rested heavily on the three, the five and the seven. They could not be set free entirely from its responsibility until such time as either the bounds were destroyed, as in the upper chamber, or one clothed with authority entering their resting place should give them their signal of release, which I did. Below the seven, the failure of conditions above absolved the members of the remaining chambers, and they

---

[16] The Council of Hermes, active only in the Hermetic Brotherhood of Atlantis. This Council, composed of Initiates, those who have been honored by the touch of the Flame, is as active today as in the past, and equally as secret. None but those who have learned to guard the tongue, and to speak only in Council, may belong to this Council. Though Love is the greatest law in the universe, these are greater, because they do not betray even through love.

were set free in a very short time after the cataclysm.

"You are well known to me as to the rest of the Ancient Brotherhood, and have been chosen again, as in the long-ago past, to be the spokesman of our beloved Order in its newest appeal to mankind, and we are sure that mistakes of the intellect in the past will not be repeated in the present. But we are approaching the ship. The most important object of our voyage, the possession of these records, which no person living or dead could obtain without your actual presence in the flesh, is accomplished. The voyage was planned and undertaken for this purpose and will result as planned. Our vessel has been lying over the entrance to the great port, at the mouth draining the Atlantian continent, from which, before the overthrow, a magnificent panorama of the fairest land the sun ever shone on was visible.

"We could not accomplish our object until near the full moon, so the calm has lasted until this time. But tonight as the sun goes down a breeze will spring up, and by tomorrow our voyage will be moving rapidly forward to its completion."

It did not occur to me, during all this recital, to object either to the facts stated or to the certain quiet assumption of myself as one of the willing accessories of the plan he had thus hastily sketched. It seemed quite a matter of course that the sole object of my making this voyage was the accomplishment of what I now, with mortal ears, for the first time heard. Nay, more, I felt a certain enthusiasm, a quiet joy in being thus permitted to do the task, whatever it might be, that was set for me, as an integral factor of the whole, to complete. I know that this is not at all the thing likely to happen, according to deduction from what we know of human nature. But as this story is one of facts on new lines, we cannot be guided by precedents or the working of known laws, as we seek rather in the fields of the unexplained laws of nature for a solution of the phenomena presented.

But we were now close to the ship, and the men were making ready to hoist the yawl aboard. As we reached the deck my friend showed his casket as a curious souvenir of the stone pile we had visited. After looking at it casually they assented to the fact: "It is a nice bit of rock; looks a trifle water-worn though." And so knowledge of incalculable value passed beyond their reach forever, or at the least until the refiner's furnace of the ages shall have prepared them more fully for the perception of that which may at any time be offered them.

CHAPTER V

As THE sun sank on the western horizon, a northeastern wind began to strain out our "idly flapping sails," and the good ship once more moved merrily over the waters.

The full moon of the tropics climbed out of the great wastes of waters, and my friend and I sat on the quarter-deck, chatting of various matters. Suddenly, as if some one had spoken to him in reminder of some event, he said, "Yes, certainly; at once."

A moment after, the stone casket, which I had seen in his cabin just before sunset, was put into his hands, coming about as fast as a man would walk, out of the companionway. At that time no one else was near us on the deck; therefore, no remarks were made.

In my peculiar state of mind this, too, seemed perfectly natural, as well as what followed.

Taking the casket in his hands, he pointed out to me several characters and symbols engraved deeply in the stone. Calling my attention to a form of the *winged globe*,[17] he said, "That is the *signet seal of him who was our most learned*, Ancient Brother. It holds the contents of the casket in trust for him who hath the password. Let us see if we may open it.

"Lay the open palm of your left hand on mine, the fingers straight, and say as thou mayest receive out of the silence. If thou art he whom I have expected to meet, it is well. If not, then it is still only patience for further waiting."

---

[17] The Symbol of the *Temple of the Rosy Cross*, the ninth grade of the Hermetic System. Freeman B. Dowd, as the Third Supreme Grand Master of the Rosicrucian Fraternity established by Randolph, was permitted to use this as his insignia or signature of authority. This is one of the *keys* to the story.

He held out his left hand, palm up. I placed my own left hand upon it, palm to palm. As I did so, a little shock passed over my whole body like an electric thrill, only a little more intense. His eyes, shining with a piercing brilliancy, caught mine. Then I felt another hand lying on the back of mine, and a form shadowed out of the thin air by my side, and simultaneously I could see the full, regal proportions of a most majestic figure standing beside us. Prominently out of the shadow, as when one feels the sun's rays, I could distinctly feel the brightness of another pair of eyes similar to those of my friend in the body.

At the same moment of time there came ringing through the air to my ears a low, musical chant. Instantly I appeared to be up-borne where beneath me a vast city lay spread out in all its beauty and glory for many leagues. We three still remained together in the same relative position. I had lost all consciousness of any difference of condition in the three present, who seemed equal in every respect. At this instant a single syllable from my friend's lips, indescribable in its intonation, arrested my attention. Without volition of my lower consciousness, in exactly the same cadence I uttered a syllable and then, like the soft, clear ringing of a silver bell, trilled from the lips of our bodyless brother the third syllable of a word[18] whose awful powers all mystics concede.

As the last note rang out into space the casket came once more fully into my consciousness. I saw it open slowly until the cover turned fully back and revealed a large roll of the finest papyrus, clearly written in plain but minute characters

---

[18] The legend of the *Holy Word* or *Ineffable Name,* potent to open *all* Doors, and powerful enough to create or destroy worlds. The legend is that no one in possession of it would use it for his own protection even in the face of death or disgrace. It is divulged to Initiates only *after* they have been tested and proved strong enough to resist the temptation itself. It is in possession only of those who belong to the Council of Hermes, or the Fifteen.

of what we have supposed was a transition period of Egyptian civilization.

My friend reverently raised the scroll from its resting place. As he did so a fragrance inimitable and of bewildering effect upon the senses poured from it. Holding this precious record of the past in his hands, he said:

"For over 29,000 years, my brother, this papyrus has not seen the light. When it was last inclosed in this casket and sealed, we three, still in the body, looked forward to the accomplishment of much that was beyond the power of limited mortal potency. I am glad to greet thee, my companion and brother. I was not mistaken in thee, for to no power but the presence of the three would the casket have yielded its contents. When I shall have read it to you it will be left in your hands for safe-keeping. Tomorrow we will begin our work, giving six of the early hours of the day to it."

CHAPTER VI

So on the next morning we commenced our tale of transfer and rescription. He translated while I wrote down in shorthand that which he thus gave me. At the first it was slowly given, owing to the fact of my being a little rusty in my stenography, but as I recalled my skill, our speed increased.

The MSS. was a full and complete record of all that concerned that wonderful country whose daring leaders, like many another seeking to manifest unusual power, have come in contact with impassable limitations and pulled down their country and involved all in irretrievable disaster, because they lacked omnipotence to carry out their designs. But I will not anticipate, but submit to my readers the history of Atlantis and the story of the secret causes that led to the final overthrow, as I have copied it from the notes of that never-to-be-forgotten voyage. It begins with an invocation by the Scribe, as follows:

"I, Tlana, Scribe of the Mighty Three, to whom it has been given strictly in charge so to do, herein write the history of my beloved country. This is to be for the instruction and enlightenment of my people when they, in the far-off ages to come, shall need more than bread, help to recurring memory. I demand for this undertaking the necessary assistance and guidance from the Brotherhood of both the Invisible and the Visible, so soon to become of the Invisible; from the gods of Wisdom and Power, and from the Supreme Ruler of All, that I may say that which is best and most instructive concerning the actions and conditions of our nation from its beginning to now [about 29,000 B.C.].

"Our continent follows the general outline of all the others now in manifestation upon the earth. It is about 1000 miles broad at its widest point and 3000 miles long at its longest dimension. The surface is mostly level, consisting of vast fertile plains. But to the west, north and east the country becomes mountainous. From these mountains, as a watershed, a river with its branches drains nearly the whole length of the continent. Its waters, diverted through an artificial canal and locks, forms the great port of the City of Atlantis, which extends from this canal, northeast of the central portion of the continent, quite up to the foothills of the elevated portion of the country. Among these mountains has been built the Great Temple dedicated to OM, who is the ONE, the All.

"Our records fail to give us any information of the beginning of man's occupancy here, and it is only through the power of perception of our wise men that we gain any idea of that beginning. It is sufficient to say, when the Fifth Race men needed a home for their unfolding, they found it here. Their unfolding has been along the lines of the strongest development. We may, therefore, simply describe the conditions now existing as the outcome of the thought-forces of the most powerful nation of the known world.

"The fertility of our soil is unparalleled anywhere upon the earth. Our difference of elevation above the sea level gives variety to our climate, and whatever grows otherwhithers on the globe will grow here also in the greatest luxuriance and perfection. We have no need to import anything grown out of the ground from other nations.

"Our supplies of minerals from the bosom of the earth are incomparable in their amount and abundance. We have all metals found anywhere upon the surface of the earth. We also have one, of which none has ever been discovered in any other country. It possesses the ductility and color of copper and the strength of iron. We have named it Orichalcum.

"The fauna holds every species of animal, which from here

has been carried to all parts of the earth, there to find a new habitat and become of use to the children of men either for labor or pleasure. This was the center of distribution. Whatever knowledge or wisdom on this line experience has given them, they have freely passed it on to those who stood in need of it. In short, whatever mankind possesses in any degree anywhere, we also possess in vast abundance far beyond our needs. Never has any State, Nation or Potentate ever before concentrated so much of wealth; that is, surplus of supplies of all kinds, as we hold today.

"No word but immense will truly describe our public works. No nation has even dreamed of a Temple like ours, much less built one. The private residences of our citizens, even of the poorer sort, outshine in beauty of design and suitableness of material the kings of many other nations. Do not consider that I am seeking to belittle others or to extol ourselves, but I am stating as fully and as candidly as I can that which is really the fact as I now write.

"The mountains have springs of hot and cold water which act as natural reservoirs. From them the water is conveyed by stone pipes to the public baths and to the private residences of such citizens as choose to avail themselves of the privilege under certain conditions.

"In the center of the city are the royal palaces, and these are protected by three immense canals, which are built entirely around them, with two intervening zones of land. These canals are connected with the Great Sea by another canal 300 feet wide and 100 feet deep and six miles long, to connect with the port.

"The Great Temple is in the northeast part of the city. Its lofty tower, bearing upon its top the finest observatory ever yet built, occupies the northeast quarter of the Temple grounds. This and the Temple itself are protected from attack on the north, east and west by the mountains, which serve both as a defense and a foundation to hold up the massive structures built upon them.

"From the mountains the city of cities extends in a circular form southward. Beyond the immense area occupied by the city proper is still another, comprising upward of 75,000 square miles, which has been cultivated from time immemorial and is, in fact, one vast garden. This is liberally irrigated from the river and from a canal 600 feet in width and 100 feet deep, extending through the country 1200 miles. Not only are these waters used for irrigation, but through a system of locks at the port galleys are raised and lowered into the grand canal, where they both receive and distribute cargoes of all kinds of products in the interests of commerce.

"It is hardly necessary to mention that the population of this plain and the mountains is many millions. Never will there be so many people gathered in the same place at the same time, so say our prophets and Magi.

"Nor must I forget to say that the volume of our population is increased by the fact that, owing to the dominance of the life-giving power of the spirit, which has not been weakened yet to any great extent, there are three or four generations of men upon the earth at the same time, all strong and vigorous. As the necessary supplies for the maintenance of the body at its best are in the greatest profusion, nature in no sense retards the increase of population, but would support to the utmost limit the most prolific increase possible.

"During the day the myriad sounds of voice and action that arise over the docks and the quarters of the city devoted to labor are like the roar of a tornado on the sea, hurling itself against the embattled rocks.

"The Atlantian galleys have reached every port and nation under the whole broad heaven. They have laid the entire surface of earth under tribute to our commerce. We have no need to ask another nation for anything we have not. But they seek from us the fruits of our soil and our incomparable bronze manufactures, in whose production our artisans have become very expert, especially in clubs, axes, knives and swords.

"The barbarians of the eastern world have never been able to make these things for themselves, and as the material and tempering of our artisans are very fine, we find market for all we can possibly offer. The only article of which we fail in making the supply equal to the demand is a bright yellow metal, which offers a powerful resistance to the action of the elements. It is eagerly sought for purposes of decoration, both of building and persons. The total product of our own mines is thus appropriated, and our traders have discovered that it exists in other parts of the world. So they seek it everywhere and when found offer our own products in exchange for it. When they bring it home they are offered certain immunities and privileges in addition to the market value for it. Thus, in a way, it has become a measure of value, not only with us, but with all the nations of the earth. It is predicted by our Magi that this peculiar condition, through the foul greed of man, will grow into a calamity for the whole race. The desire upon which its gathering by us is founded will become irrepressible and destructive in the more physical nations in the years to come. As, however, our nation has done no intentional wrong and has tried to deal justly, it can hardly be considered responsible for any such evil. It is also true that if evil does come upon the race, we shall be forced to meet it in the long ages yet to come as we are again called to face in new bodies the lives allotted to us. Thus far, strained intensity for acquisition has not acquired force enough to injure us in our development on any line.

"We are not a nation of flesh-eaters, for the warmth of our climate does not compel the concentration of food sought in the use of flesh. It is because we are not bound to the soil in our efforts to overcome the circle of necessity that we can give so much time to the study of the real forces and facts of the universe and the methods by which they could be made useful to themselves.

"At the north are three high mountain peaks, which have become landmarks for all seafaring men. In the way of review of what I have written, permit me to take my future readers to the highest summit of the great peak Alyhlo, and from thence point out the paradise of mountain and valley, hill and plain, interspersed with broad plateaux. These are covered with tropical vegetation, bearing all kinds of edible fruits known to man throughout the whole circle of the year. Limpid streams from the mountainsides water a large portion of this vast district.

"Nor is this all, for the whole picture is dotted thick with substantial dwellings, hamlets and towns. But above all is the capital as a center of interest, and an exchange of thought so wide, so far-reaching, that all the other centers in the whole country seem but suburbs.

"Notice also the varied greens of the vegetation and the blue of the sky, so clear and so perfect, as yet undisturbed in its vibrations by the shock of either offense or defense. Beyond these can be seen the canal leading to the land-locked sea and the great port with its fleets of arriving and departing galleys from every quarter of the globe. These galleys move neither by sail nor oar, nor any impulsion of elemental force. Surmounting all these, our Magi have imparted the secret of etheric impulse born of thought, and against this wind or tide has no power. It is the fairest land that man in all his generations thus far has ever seen."

CHAPTER VII

BEFORE going forward with the descriptions of the MSS. let us do a little comparing with the present situation as we now know it. The location of the ancient continent must have covered in part the Caribbean Archipelago. If the land were so raised as to make the highest peak six miles high, there must have resulted two immense inland seas where now is the Gulf of Mexico. Across these and the old continent would blow in constant succession the trade winds, bringing moisture and fertility upon their broad wings for the teeming population. In configuration there must have been a striking resemblance to our upper lake country.

The range of mountains to the west and north must have constituted the backbone of the continent, whose peaks and table-lands now form a chain of islands. On the line of drainage from the inland sea the Amazon must now be located. The fertility must have been the result not so much of a torrid temperature as of the absence of cold winds, which gave a peculiar, equable, life-developing climate, both for vegetables and animals. Everything possible grew, because there were no drawbacks to its growth. It was always seedtime; it was always harvest. Bud, blossom and fruit in all their different stages of maturity could be seen growing at once on the same tree. What is partially true today of the orange and lemon was then true of all fruit-bearing trees. So fertile was the original condition of the soil and so great the wisdom of those who directed that the matter of planting seed and gathering harvest became a matter of sequence and not of season. With this explanation let us return to our manuscript:

"The change of condition from life to death is one accepted and welcomed by our people; not in any sense feared, because during their long-continued existence the monotony of physical life is fully satisfied, and the only inducement for accepting prolongation is the increasing of the spirit's force and potency with which we are well acquainted and fully educated as to its limitless possibilities.

"Our place as carriers for the world has for many years been acknowledged. On all seas and in every port are the galleys that supply the world's marts, flying the Atlantian flag—a winged globe[19] in blue on a yellow ground. It, therefore, happens in our ample harbor the myriad swarms of shipping, although loaded with the products of the whole earth, are ours.

"The sailors of other nations dare not move out into the vast wastes of waters separating the different countries one from another.

"Great warehouses lie along the water's edge, which is bordered from the sea for many miles into the interior by immense, solidly built walls. These are raised high enough to be above any high-water mark of either flood from the interior or tide from the ocean. But floods were rather the result of changes in the amount of drainage, for the melting of snow on the mountains or increase of amount from suddenly precipitated vapor was a thing of but slight importance.

"The capital is connected with all parts of the kingdom by iron tramways, upon which enormous loads are moved by a motive force whose secret only our Magi know. But the obedient force moves back and forth, drawing and pushing, as it is bidden by its controller, the heavily laden wagons to which it is harnessed.

"The whole city is built of a pure white marble, taken from quarries in the Northern Hills, whose supplies are used not

---

[19] Symbolic of spiritual attainment. The Winged Globe represents the Soul in flight, the Soul in freedom; as also that of full consciousness or Illumination of the Soul—Immortalization. It was on the escutcheon of every member of Hermes, or the Council of Fifteen.

only for building at home, but also for export. So fine is the grain and so elegant the polish that the blocks are used over and over in rebuilding in the cities of the Mediterranean. This stone cannot endure the extremes of temperature of the northern climate, but is amply strong for all that may be demanded under an Atlantian sky.

"From what I have already said, perhaps it will be plain the city is laid out like a disc, with a segment wanting, where it is fitted against the foothills of the northern mountain ranges.

"Broad avenues in semi-circle begin at the mountains and end in the mountains. These are crossed at regular intervals by other avenues, forming the radii of the circle, the center of which is the King's palace. There is no ownership of land, save in the King's name as the representative of the nation. It is held by our Magi that no man can own anything in which his own labor or some representative thereof does not constitute a component part. All articles of handiwork, therefore, can be claimed by the contributors thereto, but man has not attained, and can never attain, ownership in the four great elements of manifestation—fire, air, water, earth. If he ever shall attempt it, disaster and degradation will attend the attempt. If a man builds a house or plants a tree, or cultives a crop, then the house or tree or harvest belongs to him,[20] and he should be protected in his right to enjoy fully all that can come from his labor.

"All lands are parceled out by lot, and only the improvements have a price. He who would like his neighbor's location must, with his neighbor's consent, buy the improvements, but the land has no more value than the air about it.

"The houses are built for convenience and comfort. Every

---

[20] The rights of ownership—private property rights. An absolute Law. Any concerted attempt to destroy this right will ultimately result in the destruction of democratic nations and reduce all but the few egomaniacs to the status of slaves.

family owns its own home,[21] and when a young man takes to himself a wife he has a portion of land assigned him under conditions which make equable all inequalities of place, quality or surroundings. No crowding is allowed, not even in the thickest part of the city. The buildings are of permanent material, fashioned to let in the air and light. The underlying principle is a central open court, with the living rooms all about it. This plan is modified in many ways to suit the individualities and needs of the owners.

"The court is entered by a broad gate, swinging easily on its ample fittings. In the center a pool with an overflowing fountain to prevent stagnation cools the air and helps modify the vibrations. The water was supplied by an aqueduct from the mountains. This was so old that no Atlantian of the present people can give its age. But there are records in the archives of the Temple concerning the planning of the huge undertaking and the manner of its accomplishment. About this pool the building stands, generally two stories, so supported on pillars as to form no obstruction to free movement of the air.

"When the young couple decide to locate, it is the custom to receive from the chief astrologer of the Temple a horoscope definitely naming the number of the new family to come. For each one a room was built in the home. This special allotment prevents crowding and is productive to the utmost of progress and growth on all lines.

"Animals herd, man individualizes in his tendency.[22] At

---

[21] The ultimate aim is that all men shall own and maintain their own individual domicile. In the ideal nation, this law will be fundamental and exploitation will cease, because the owner cannot create any indebtedness which endangers the home, nor will there be any means whereby he may be defrauded of it.

[22] As man proceeds in his development he becomes more individualistic. This does not bring about selfishness, nor lack of feeling toward others. On the contrary, as man individualizes he advances upward; he brings into potent manifestation his forces and energies; he becomes a beacon, a light, for all others to follow, until all men shall become like

either end of the scale, acceptation of or rebellion against the herding indicates where he stands at any given time as regards either his spiritual or his physical nature. If he is inclined to be brutish, it matters not if fifty hands, eating with his, dip into the same bowl of porridge. If he is spiritually unfolded, he would prefer to appropriate and use in his own way that which comes belonging to and prepared especially for himself. This is not, as it might at the outset appear, selfishness, but is the outcropping of the work which the Ego takes upon itself during the earth lives, the soul-building out of the incarnations.

"The rooms on the first story are larger and mostly used for the offices of living, in which the family relations are concerned and perfected. Most of their leisure time is spent about the fountain in the court, where there are always agreeable shadows with the blue sky above. The courts are paved in colored patterns with a kind of glass and carpeted with rugs and mats woven from vegetable textiles and fancifully dyed. These goods are made principally for export. Besides these furnishings, there are, side by side, products of man's thought from every part of the earth, the richest and the best. None are blood-

---

the gods. The herding or grading of men into a common lot destroys all incentive; the nation profits for a time, but ultimately the highest is *no greater* than *the lowest,* and man collectively has returned to the status of the beast and the nation is subdued by the more virile races and is enslaved for the dominant race's advancement. This has been the history of all nations which have risen to greatness and then sunk to servility because of defiance of the law which proclaims that to "the laborer belongs the reward," and the term "labor" refers not alone to the "sweat of the brow," but more especially to the development of mind and Soul. An army of a million valiant soldiers without a leader might readily be annihilated by another army of a hundred thousand men under the direction of a trained mind. Therefore, the trained mind of one man has an equal, if not a greater, value than that of a million untrained men. The *eternal* Law recognizes *not* the man *per se,* BUT WHAT HE MAKES OF HIMSELF, *i.e.,* how he individualizes himself. On the contrary, the man who destroys individualization *destroys initiative,* and ALL MEN BECOME OF THE COMMON HERD—HIS SLAVES. Let us think on this, and never permit ourselves to forget it, lest we perish as have all men before us.

stained as the spoils of war, for our traffic, industrious and honorable, has made us beyond peradventure the richest nation that ever existed upon the earth.

"From the first, we have traded everywhere. No galley of ours has ever been seized by the god of the seas and left lying upon the ocean bottom, whether bearing our goods forth or bringing back to us the merchandise of other lands. This natural increase by labor and by trade, without loss, should of itself have been sufficient to have enriched us without other means.

"Thus it is perceived the families are by themselves; each is an independent community. Their houses and gardens are as much the kingdom of that community as can possibly be conceived.[23] This is the rule of the spiritual and not of the physical.

"But I must not forget to speak of the streets and roads of the city proper and the outlying country. These are laid out on a certain general plan which, once established, has never been changed. Although they have been many years in construction and extension, every foot has been added under the direction of a master mind in conformity to a uniform plan adopted thousands of years ago. So far as they are extended, they are finished and lasting. The substance used for the roadbeds is our secret of the whole world. Our ways are dustless and noiseless. The peculiar composition readily yields traction to bodies moving over them. Never has there been so perfect a system of easy transportation upon the earth.

"The public buildings are always large, roomy and of varied

---

[23] This is the Ideal State. In no wise does this indicate that each man is a law unto himself in so far as the community or the state is concerned, but that each is obedient to a common law and works in harmony with that law to the common good. When this is done then few laws are necessary in governing the common mass, it being a truism that the people least governed are best governed.

styles, surmounted with domes, pinnacles and minarets and ornamented with statues of artistic design and workmanship. The material of which these are built is white marble. Atlantis can well claim not only the honor of being so created, but of remaining a white city. There is no darkening effluvium in the air nor the climate to obscure the white walls set in the great billows of surrounding green. Our Magi say that in days to come a nation on the Mediterranean Sea called the Greeks will personify in their works of art our beloved city as a beautiful woman rising from the sea.

"The more important of these buildings are profusely decorated with gold, and it is for this purpose that metal is so eagerly bought by the Atlantian traders. A poetical name—'the tears of the sun'[24]—has been adopted by our people, and by this it is most widely called here. Of the palace of the King, of the Great Temple, I will speak more at length by and by.

"In these public buildings are rooms for social meetings, to discuss public topics and for the convenience of classes studying things that do not belong to the physical plane. A description of one will be a description of the general plan of all. They are elliptical in form, with a fountain in the center. The Atlantians are extravagantly fond of the presence of water. At one of the foci are a number of seats, arranged like an amphitheater, built of stone and rising one above another. At the other of the foci stands a Tribune, upon which the speaker stands when public addresses are made. About the fountain also are seats where the auditors sit easily and converse one with another.

"In like manner are built the training schools of the young, the central part of the structure being open to the sunlight and

---

[24] In our time this is changed to "the tears and passions of the people," and because of this metal men have committed every crime that the human mind can conceive, and no degradation is too great in the gaining of it.

the air. Here the young Atlantians are educated in the things that belong to the nation, the family and to themselves. Our fathers had a saying we seek to make a rule of living: 'Eight years to infancy and play, eight years to boyhood and training in physical things, eight years to young manhood and learning of the world outside of Atlantis, and one thousand years to learning of the invisible and real.' Its proportions are very nearly correct.

CHAPTER VIII

"THE Atlantians of either sex are almost perfect in their physical organizations. They are nearly all equally trained by the master of wisdom. It may be asked why they are not all on the same plane of development. The reply is the conclusive answer of all ages and times. Man never has and never will exercise his individual potency in exactly the same way. The little variation, hardly perceptible at first, is increased by every increment, no matter how small, of each of the succeeding lives. This difference is increased also by the force of intellectual power which comes to a nation and of necessity to the individuals of the nation who will seek to occupy the best bodies and positions as the returning egos claim place in the lives.[25]

"Because of the absolute equality of the sexes, the bodies of the women are just as strong and vigorous as those of the men. But we know that in other nations with which we have come in contact in other parts of the world the women are inferior in

---

[25] Therefore the crime of destroying individuality. Every person is a unit in himself and a law in his own right. Unity in diversity is the law. No two people can possibly be alike. Some minds and Souls are ages old and have stored within them the wisdom of the ages. Given a fair opportunity, these become the geniuses and masters of the age, working for a common goal and leading others upward. When their individuality is inhibited and they are prevented from outstripping, *by right of fitness,* their fellow-men so as to act as magnets drawing the mass forward, the whole mass suffers and falls as does dough when the leaven is allowed to grow cold before the mass has risen. There can be no Brotherhood of Man at this age based *on equality.* It must be a Brotherhood of service, of the *equal rights* of all men, the fortunate lending a helping hand to the less fortunate; the wise being guides to the foolish, the strong as crutches for the weak. Nor is there any man fit to be absolute dictator of a people unless they have sunk so low as to be incapable of self-government—of directing their own actions. At best, the greatest man can be no more than a wise director and protector of the rights of all.

size and strength. This happens because the people of those nations have allowed themselves, from generation to generation and from age to age, to believe in and assert the inferiority of women. This continued thought has belittled and dwarfed her, not only in body, but has also bound her aspirations and her mental capacity with bonds stronger than steel. While the barbarian races, to their sorrow and loss, have made this sad mistake, the Atlantian nation, on the other hand, has constantly held to the equality of the sexes. The result now is, physically, both sexes are models which painter or sculptor are proud and eager to copy. Each one is a specimen of beauty, for perfection is beauty. The action of the climate and transmitted principles have brought intellectual vigor and daring with a marvelous grasp of perception upon the laws of nature and of themselves. Their bodies, instead of being impediments to spiritual growth and advancement, are helps, indeed, to the spirits who seek through them experience, knowledge and understanding. Those who might be called the common class, doing the necessary labor of the nation, are far advanced beyond the literary class of the barbarian nations in their perception of the truth and their knowledge of nature's laws. The day will come in the future when men will mourn this knowledge forgotten, when the fatigue and monotony of burden-bearing will be almost overwhelming in its crushing awfulness.

"We have schools for the development of the physical and for the directing of the mental habits of thought. In these schools very little memorized knowledge is imparted. The design is to so train the faculties that, if desired or needed, the cipher of the Astral books could easily be read.

"Sickness is unknown. We have no lame, halt, blind, deaf or dumb or beggars as models for maternal pre-natal mind to misform embryos and thus build monstrosities for the public charge. This of which I speak is true of the nations who are busy in the affairs of commerce, of agriculture or who are builders and decorators of houses and public buildings. But there are some who, from natural impulsion, have sought more and more of the invisible, of the truths which belong to the ONE, and those who rest in IT. These are willing and anxious to devote themselves and their powers constantly to obtaining and attaining and the teaching of youth. The only class distinction we have is founded upon knowledge.

"It has come to pass in a natural fashion that these thinkers have gravitated toward one another; that they have kept records of observation, experiment and experience; that they are wiser in speech; in mathematics as applied to the unseen; in alchemy, in astrology, and they are specially wise in the physics which embrace the laws of the unseen. At first buildings were set apart for these students and their teachers. As the city grew, each body of students had its building, now known as temples. Later all were gathered into the one great Temple in order that the symbolism of the ONE who is ALL might be perfect.

"In the teachings of our Magi, all manifestation on all planes is referred back to the ONE as the single central source of strength and power for everything obtained and obtainable. Thus the mind dwelling on this thought has striven in design, in material, in finishing and furnishing to make the Great Temple a perfected symbol of the ONE. Its worship in all its imagery and suggestion combines every element for the impressiveness of mode and subject under discussion upon the minds of the student. Is it any wonder that there has come to us as a nation a deep-seated veneration for the Omnipotent name and laws?

"It is also a fact that our Magi are in possession of most wonderful powers in the control of elemental forces who obey their will, coming to their tasks not under confinement, but

because obedient to the will and behest of those who call singly
or unitedly for their services. It is also known that this power
never will be held except by Atlantian-born people, regardless
of the changing conditions of the globe.

"It is also true that a far greater proportion of our people
have attained to the superior light and knowledge than any
other nation upon the earth either in the past or present. This
is doubtless due to the fact that our incarnating egos, having
the right of choice,[26] have again and again sought their own
people as the most privileged spot in which to make advancement during their lives.

"When these advanced egos have found their bodies we have
the spectacle of children born old, for the brightness of the last
life is heavy on them, and the newness of the body does not
always act as a defense or shield from its imperious blaze. It
is not in each, but is a matter of ordinary, detailed development.

---

[26] All advanced or developed Souls have this right of choice, and it is
for this reason that the higher spiritual training has always been and
continues to be so desirable. Because of it, men cease to be pawns on
the chessboard of life and become the players, ever moving toward race
advancement and the elimination of weakness and degradation. In this
wise alone, by the refinement of the individual, can race salvation become an actual fact.

CHAPTER IX

"WE HAVE but one basic law throughout called the 'golden rule,' or preference of another before self. We have no evils arising out of the action of selfishness, for this condition is the primary result of the fear of destitution, either for ourselves or others, some time during the position or period of earth-life. Even they who are the least advanced understand from our teaching the true idea of Brotherhood; that no man, no man's wife, no man's children, can, under the law, suffer from deprivation of the necessities of physical life. He who has more than enough is held to be always the steward in trust for him who temporarily has less than enough. But this does not relieve from the necessity of labor,[27] of every individual in the direct ratio of their ability, at whatever employment they are best fitted.

"In the building of our houses, the quarrying of the stones, the transportation and the fitting are all done by elemental force,

---

[27] In modern times, in periods of stress, numerous nations have tried what is commonly known as the "dole." This has, in all instances, led to the weakening of the moral and responsible nature of the individual accepting; therefore in like manner affecting the nation. Man is in general so constituted that he will not assume responsibility unless compelled to do so by necessity. As a result, men become weaklings and dependents if this necessity is removed, as it is where people are given a stipend for their maintenance, without demanding a full return in exchange. Men in distress should be helped over the rough places, as should business concerns when in need. But, just as a business concern, even though employing many men, when in dire financial distress, *must give collateral* and, in a sense, barter all its possessions in exchange for the help required, so should the individual in need be required to give his note of hand to repay the loan made to him just as quickly as he is in a position to do so. In this manner would men be compelled to assume their personal responsibility for that which they receive, and the amount accepted would be held down to a minimum. Likewise would manhood and the morale of the people be maintained and kept to a high standard.

under the direction of a master who is in charge of a section. It is his duty to educate them and to see that they are duly provided for, out of the Astral storehouse, by the power given into his hands. The form of government has already been copied from us by a powerful nation in the Northern part of Asia, but because of their situation on the physical plane, it is most likely they will be able to retain only the form and will lose the spiritual power which is the foundation and potent principle.

The whole nation is linked together by the master of the families; these are in groups and classes, under instruction and direction from those who are most competent to teach. These teachers are grouped under the masters or Magi of the Temple. These Magi of the Temple are under the instruction of the Most Ancient, the Seven, the Five and the Three. So, in the hands of the Three, mightiest of all human intellects, rest the destinies, the prosperity and the happiness of the whole nation. Moreover, upon them as directors and arbiters the responsibility of Karmic conditions rested, as they were engendered by the currents of potency issuing from themselves, and, returning upon their cycle, bore with them whatever had been impressed upon or mingled with them during their revolvement among those to whom the currents were sent.

"It must be apparent to whom this MSS. may come that the powers of the Unseen and their application to man's earth-life are matters of the greatest interest and importance to the Atlantians. There is no temporal power, save as a symbol of the Manifested. Everything pertaining to organized effort originates with and is carried forward by the Priesthood of the Great Temple, which represents the dominant power over matter of the spirit at its highest and best. They have specially in charge the study and development of all Occult knowledge.

"Every house is independent of itself. The Atlantians are Monogamists—the one husband of one wife. This experience has demonstrated to be the best condition for the development of a strong, spiritual race. We have seen that polygamous races always decrease in power, strength and energy of purpose.

"In Atlantis, to be diseased or crippled in body, or to be at the head of a family in which is such a member, is deemed a crime against the people. Therefore, all thought, all desire and interest are brought to bear upon physical conditions, through Occult and spiritual forces, not only to make the nation whole, but whole in the highest and best sense.

"Those who are particularly gifted with psychic qualities or whose spirits have attained familiarity with the instrument intrusted to their hands are trained for the offices of Masters or Guides. These may or may not have families, but in either case they are persons to whom a certain number of persons or families look for counsel, advice and guidance.

"For thousands of years have the Magi of the Temple, who give their whole time to the study of the Unseen and lay aside their bodies at their own volition, really placed the welfare and best good of the people beyond any other consideration whatever. The nation is happy. They have no poor. They have no inferior class. All necessary labor is honorable. Generation after generation, we have been growing stronger and more like the gods come down to earth. We have perfect communication with the outside world and each other. We know Atlantis is the fairest city on the planet, and we are content."

CHAPTER X

HAVING thus far advanced in the description of the most wonderful city ever known to man, permit me to quote from the words of one who saw what he so fluently and graphically describes for you:

"To the northeast of this island continent is located the Great Temple, built both for use and symbolism. On a plateau of many acres in extent, where the gradually rising ground began to break into the foothills, the whole surface had been leveled and paved with some soft material, of which the Atlantians alone knew the secret. This hardened under the action of the sun and atmosphere until it was like adamant. To the east, a belt of country reaching to the seacoast, but not on a level with it, had also been smoothed and paved, so that there was no obstruction to the eye until it rested on the far-off horizon.

"Upon this broad expanse of level space, close enough to the mountains to be buttressed by their mighty arms, stood the great, white-walled Temple, facing the south, and the ample areas for assemblage. The closed courts and offices and the cloisters of the Temple faced the mountains of the north and thus secured for the Temple Dwellers the privacy needed for the Masters and student Brotherhoods of the Temple who were seeking to know out of the Silence.

"The Temple proper consists of two stories, the first one consisting of pillars springing from the rocky foundations of the mountain and supporting arches, which in turn held up immense slabs of stone, the floors of the second story. On the first floor there is little or no inclosure, but within the walls of the second story it is all arranged for privacy and quiet thought. He who looks over the battlements of the upper story looks down about ninety feet into the beautifully paved court below. On the east and west of the Temple itself are gardens, groves of trees, fountains, running streams of water, domesticated animals, and flowers of every hue and fragrance. These are sacred to the Temple, but open to the people under the surveillance of the caretakers, except certain reserved spots close to the Temple, which are for the special use of the students and teachers. In the northeast section of the Temple building was the great tower and observatory, fifty feet in diameter, rising 210 feet, a landmark and light extending hundreds of miles and ever a joy-inspirer for the sea-tossed mariners of the State.

"Looking from the plaza in front, toward the interior of the Temple, its vast recesses, its forests of white pillars and its high-lifted over-arching roof fill the spectator with awe. Nor was this feeling lessened by the cleanliness, the continuous shifting of huge masses of sunlight and shadow ever into new and indescribable grotesquerie. During the services the awful solemnity evoked was of a character that modified the whole Atlantian thought and national purpose.

"The great tower was commenced fifteen feet below the surface. The original trap rock was supplemented by a square block of concrete rock, and upon this was carried up the superstructure to a total height of 225 feet, the square of fifteen. Upon the floor of the Temple resting on a raised dais was the secret chamber of the Holy of Holies. Across and through this, at High Festivals, blazed and flashed the Veil of Isis. Above, on a level with the upper floor, was the chamber of the Forty-five, and still above that the chambers of the Fifteen, the Seven, the Five and the Three. In the outer, the Tower was smooth and unpenetrated on its surface from bottom to top. It resembled a solid block, chiseled out of quarries and set on end, so deft was the workmanship and so perfect the joinings and finish.

"In the cloisters and rooms of the second story of the Temple were the apartments for private study and class instruction. There were also supplemental apartments, hollowed out of the neighboring mountains and reached by secret passages so arranged that whatever should be deposited in them as treasuries would be securely held, even if buried beneath the surface of the sea for ages.

"Beyond the great plaza, toward the city, trees and fountains shaded and beautified clear up to the naked edge of the vast pavement."

This is a faint portrayal of that which was really the culmination and concentration of the Nation's thousands of years of existence and unfolding.

"In all our Temples, and more especially in the Great Temple, the outer courts were but the simple separation from those who have no inspiration for the inner and higher. In the outermost court, or court of the people, were always gathered those who had thoughts of their own and who were undecided as to what direction they should take in pursuit of the light slowly dawning upon them.

"The inner court of the people contained those who have so far perceived that they are willing to obligate themselves to carry out certain purposes, of whose full intent they can know but little, except that the farther end is lost in the light of life and the halo of obligation. In this court they who seek must be fitted by training and preparation for that which lies before them, so it is natural that they who linger there, striving to advance, must do whatever they can through their own power of assimilation, by themselves.

"At the first, if the lesson is concentration, it is their individual concentration. If the lesson is passivity, it is their own individual passivity. It is exactly as when one is learning to sing. As a beginning, the voice is trained to use its own peculiar function alone. After this solitary practice, when some aptitude has been attained and a facility of use, then they are ready for the massing of singles for a united effort. It must follow, then, that the outer court of the Brotherhood cannot but lap over into the inner court of the Temple.

"That which is done singly and alone is absolutely necessary for the next step in advance, which is to be made in unison with another or others in the same way as musical students are trained by twos and fours for united efforts of action and harmony.

"The question considered in all this is, how shall growth and attainment be best accomplished? What is the basic principle?

"In music we say the sounds are set to a certain key, and however prolonged the action of the vibrations, the key and time will be the same, and all the vibrations are aligned. It is exactly thus when the students come to act together on the Occult planes. The vibrations which they produce will not, of course, be alike, but they must chord, the parts of one vibration fitting and filling in with the vibrations of another, so there shall be no jangle.

"To get the best results it is always best that they who are in the outer court of the Brotherhood should be watchful and careful lest the vibrations sent forth from themselves should be hastened or intensified or even drag through the thoughtlessness of their own carelessness.

"When once unity of action is attempted in this matter it is absolutely necessary to success that the key on which they start should remain the same.

"It is easy to see how intense passions, such as anger or any of the disturbing conditions, would interfere with the vibrations. It would be like a chord out of tune in a stringed instrument, where, though the strings do not give out the same sounds, still they must be in alignment. This alignment is the source of all music.

"It is not needful that the most intense feelings of one's nature should be given rein and allowed to make disturbance, both for himself and those whom he is contacting. It is also, on a small scale, like the sharping and flatting at the wrong points, whereby the vibrations are changed, the harmony broken and discord becomes perceptible.

"It is also absolutely necessary that all conditions in the outer which can cause a disturbance should be held in abeyance when one desires to concentrate, in order that during a united effort for concentration the harmony and strength shall not be marred. This is true of all work on any Occult line.

"It is not to be supposed, when two or more of the Brothers are concentrating, exactly the same process is gone through within the mind of each. That would be impossible. The end sought for can be attained by each working in his own way with the same thought. It does not follow, because A does not perform his task exactly as B does, that B should set up a disturbance in the vibration as reflected from A, thus in a measure destroying the co-operation and effect to be produced.

"The law of the Temple, then, is first, alone; second, in company with those who are seeking by united force to accomplish, as the Masters of Destiny at all times have been able to accomplish. Unity of action is most important. Therefore, we must guard against anything that can disturb this unity. If vibrations in their normal conditions lay along side by side and one is hastened, then the harmony is destroyed, and the action of the impulse is to increase the vibrations in the length of their wave force. We must, when meeting for united effort, insist that each for themselves shall become their own guardians. Knowing that disagreeable things will occur, we must be ever prepared at once to put them aside. Having done this once, we shall be stronger to continue. Thus the music from our Soul's action will not only affect ourselves, but those about us.

"Upon this statement of principles has been built the great law of the Temple: 'Do unto others as you would have them do unto you.' All the teaching and training, all the ceremonies and symbolism of the Temple, are founded upon this law as the cornerstone of the religion of our people. Having given this brief summary of the truths our priesthood have in charge, let us pass on to a description of some of the ceremonies of the Temple service, and as an illustration we will take the Great Feast of the New Year as more fully including the whole than any other.

"The feast of the New Year, on the 21st of March, consummated and commemorated the Sun's rebirth, when out of equal days and nights a new Spring and Summer began for the northern hemisphere, and the promise of seedtime and harvest was renewed.

"At this celebration it is expected that every family in the kingdom should be present, either personally or represented by some member of the family. All the going and coming of the year is planned with this in view. It is considered a privilege for all the outlying population to be made welcome in the capital at this time. The feast lasts seven days.

"Let me attempt to describe at length, for no pen can truly portray all the wonders of that marvelous assemblage, one of the last feasts which took place ten years before the destruction of the city. The government and people were at that time in their most perfect unity.

"About three days before the set date of the feast there could be noticed a little stir of preparation all over the country. It was a quiet movement toward participation. If one had been lifted above, so he could have looked upon the continent as upon a map, there would have been perceived during these three days long lines of travelers, some on foot and others by every method of conveyance, moving upon the city in converging lines. As the time grew shorter, the extent of these lines grew shorter, and the ways close to the city and in the city itself were filled to overflowing. There were but few people in the outlying country who had not some friend or relative in the city proper. When the houses were filled, tents were spread in the gardens and in all the parks and places of assembly. Thus there was a new appearance given to the light by its reflection from the tents, which were some of linen and some of cotton, but all bleached very white by a process known only to the Atlantians and never imparted to any other nationality. Only on the great plateau of the Temple and the areas of the outer courts, no tents were allowed, for that space was necessarily kept clear, that there might be room for the greater assembly.

"As the ceremonies were in commemoration of the new-born sun, the hours of assembly were morning and evening and at the moment of the meridian height. On the first day of the feast, as the dawn brightened in the east, out of the early twilight there could be heard throughout the whole city a low, muffled sound like the pouring of a swift torrent through a smooth bed; and as soon as it was light enough to see, all the outer courts and the great plateau of the Temple could be perceived crowded with those who had arrived to take part in the inauguration ceremonies. Their faces were turned toward the east, between whose far horizon and the eyes of the numberless watchers no obstruction intervened.

"When the moment approaches for the appearance of the Ruler of the Day, a low, sweet harmony, sounding in rhythmic change, welled out upon the air in slow, restful time and far-reaching tones from the great Temple choir, who were gathered in one of the porches of the Temple, so raised as to be seen by all the vast multitude. As the sounds of the chant, gradually swelled by the voices of the worshippers, became more intense in power and heavier in volume, all the vast multitude seemed to sway under the psychic spell of this invocation to the Sun; this symbol of welcome to one who returns to his work and purpose. The minutes move quickly on; the invocation is finished, a blast of trumpets accompanying the final note. The orb of day, with tropical suddenness, springs from his bed beneath the sea. As his first beams fall upon the countless multitude, they drop upon their knees. With bowed heads, in silent adoration, they ascribe all glory, all power, all praise to that which stands to them as the manifested source of life, of health, of strength, the ever-sleepless eye of the One. Then they separate. The hours are spent in social converse or the abandonment of rest and quiet until it is high noon.

"As the Sun approaches the meridian, all the streets and byways, all the housetops in all places where there may be a worshipper, behold his face turned toward the Temple. At the moment of meridian altitude, above the highest pinnacle, a crystal ball, almost as dazzling in its brilliancy as the sun itself, shoots up and for a few moments receives the concentrated thought of all the faithful throughout the city as the reminder of the good messenger of the One, the height of whose glory is now perceived. Again in the evening there is a convocation at the Temple. The ceremonies of the morning are repeated, with the exception that the song is one of farewell, the multitude facing the west instead of the east; and the hushing sounds of stringed instruments attend his exit from the western horizon.

"These ceremonies are continued for six days. There are various other ceremonies which take up the time of portions of the convocation between these assemblies of the whole. There are also lines of Temple services, work and study, each of the sciences having its appropriate place and each being developed by those who are allied in the great Brotherhood of the Temple. This embraced the whole people in its ramifications. It is not necessary to describe these in all their minutiæ. But during these six days there was continually something taking place in the city, always having its moving force at the Temple. The moving of a procession through the streets, a convening of the Temple guides or guards, lectures and talks from those who were so well qualified to give forth from full fountains to the inner Souls, eager to be fed. But as the evening draws on after the waning of the sixth day, once more all the courts of the Temple were thronged. The hum of conversation dies away as the darkness grows more and more intense.

"Now, when it shall have become quite dark, the Temple choir opens the exercises with the song of invocation. It differs from all the music of the convocation hitherto in key, rhythm and time. In this all the people join. As the sound vibrates in swelling cadence, rising and falling amongst the echoing mountains, the effect was perfectly indescribable, for the Atlantians were especially celebrated for being sweet singers. When the singing was finished the chief instructor of the people stood upon a Tribune high raised and there discoursed of the things which concerned them most intimately in the physical life; of whatever they stood most in need; of how the Sun was to them life and health and plenty and peace, the sign and representative of all good. Then he directed their attention to the darkness which sat so uneasily upon them, enforcing rest and inability to work. Then his peroration was after this fashion:

"The darkness is death and desolation, and thus in the beginning the Existence saw when he said, 'Let there be, and there was, light.' At this word millions of lights gleamed out all over the Temple, inside, outside, even on the highest points. It stood forth one blaze of white marble glory, for there was only one thing about electricity the Atlantians did not know, that is the point where knowledge lays hold with potency upon the One in its inmost and supreme integrity of existence.

"There are other ceremonies of minor importance pertaining to the night, but this is the most important. There are no sacrifices, no shedding of the blood of animal or human victims. The Atlantians do not believe it is necessary to teach destruction or destructive action by such sacrifice in the burning or destroying of any living thing, for they say man is naturally destructive, and we ought to teach him the opposite. So all our ceremonies lacked the hideous shadow of agony and horror that will be sure to come if man forgets our teachings. But the great object lessons served well their purpose in elevating the whole people to the same level and cementing them into a common Brotherhood. In the next chapter I will describe as well as I may the last great day of the Feast.

CHAPTER XI

"THAT of which I am now to speak concerns the Atlantian nation when there was for it seemingly nothing more beyond in glory, prosperity or knowledge. I am warned of the Unseen not to write unguardedly, but with circumspection, lest there come power for mischief to the unobligated.

"In the olden days, when step by step we had painfully and laboriously climbed the mountain heights into the broad blaze of the everlasting truth, the world lay at our feet. That was our intellectual and physical status. Whatever there was in the earth itself worth having or knowing was in our possession as the birthright of ages and ages of previous existence.

"Furthermore, we coming into life are not clouded, as the generations to come will be, by physical conditions which will grow thicker and heavier all along the pathway of the unrolling centuries. It will be because, having dominated whatsoever there may be of physical workings, we shall have sought also to master that which belongs only to the spiritual realm that we shall be cut off. There is but one God. None created can sit in the seat of the uncreated. None who exist by the thought of the Infinite One can hope to explain that which is of itself the Existent, the Cause of all results manifested or unmanifested.

"In the first part of the development of the Atlantian nation all communication was carried on by outer sense vibration, even as now. Perhaps the vibrations were not as intense as at the present, but in the latter days they who are instructed are taught by thought transference.

"The education of the young is not along the line of simple memorizing. Nor is it only the unfolding of partially physical senses. It does not appeal to material sense for the building of the Soul. We do not hope that out of bodily conditions we can bring any help to the spiritual, for we know whatever belongs to and lies along the line of the physical, rising to the highest source within itself, can rise no higher than that point. More than that, the physical in its most perfect form begets weakness and death. How can there be anything beyond this but weakness and death?

"This is one of our axiomatic doctrines. In manifestation we simply see an exemplification of that which occurred on the spiritual plane.

"In the days to come the professor of mathematics will state an axiom or a proposition and then, going to the blackboard, and upon it, appealing to the sense of sight, will demonstrate in manifestation the impression he seeks to make of the secret workings of the force beyond. If he is a chemist, he will bring before his hearers certain elements, and out of the unions of these elements, out of the separation of the conditions, there will grow up or manifest themselves certain, perhaps startling, conditions. But that which then takes place is not the truth he is trying to prove; it is simply a demonstration of the truth. Nor is the professor of mathematics trying to show you the truth. He will simply be trying to prove that to be true which he has learned from the physical side.

"Do not confound that which is unmanifested with the manifested. The unmanifested is the cause of everything manifested. The manifested exists because the unmanifested is its primal cause, reaching down through all the ages. So we do not in these days linger over demonstrations or in any way try to prove by simple manifestation the existence of the invisible and unmanifested.

"But the first course of training our students receive is a line of strengthening for their mentality. If there are those who are so physically constituted that the machinery of their thought, the power by which they could receive of the force outside of themselves, is in any way unfit or incompetent, they are first treated by the thought of those who are about them to bring them up into a healthful condition, as it is termed, on the physical plane. Really the condition is simply one of harmony."

The knowledge which has come in these latter days to us who have the pleasure of perusing this manuscript, variously named "the science of spiritual conditions—mental science—science of truth—science of knowing"—call it what you will, is really a glimpse gotten hold of by one who was clear-sighted and who in the development of the idea has manifested the bravery of the old Soul. It is only to these old Souls are intrusted the works that will stir every man's heart that hears of them. It is, however, by standing before the world and demonstrating for years and years that which is the germ-cell of a most wonderful knowledge, the unfolding along invisible and spiritual lines can be accomplished. But I must not forget to state that the privilege of giving out these truths so that they can be understood belongs to the Atlantian-born.

If these stand in their places today and declare their personal knowledge to be truth until that truth is recognized, they have done for themselves a service—it matters not whether the clouds and thick darkness may inclose them afterward. That portion of the truth which they have put forth will stand forever and forever. So what we know as an occasional matter of healing after a miraculous fashion was a thing of everyday occurrence with the Old Atlantians. Those who united for the purpose of increasing the race mated themselves first according to the best knowledge belonging to the astrologers of those days. Thus mated, it rarely happened, as one of our poets hath sung: "Deformed, unfinished, sent before my time into this breathing world, scarce half made up," was the fate of any-one born of woman. When any unripeness of this kind appeared it was treated successfully on the mental plane.[28]

---

[28] A mental picture of health, vitality and well-being is placed before the mind's eye, or psyche, of the ill or imperfect person, and this perfect picture gradually becomes a part of the psyche of that person and, as this progresses, it becomes manifest throughout the physical being and well-being or physical perfection is established. This is the highest form of physical reconstruction and will ultimately again become part of the services both physicians and ministers will render their followers. In the Higher Occult this is known as Image Formation, Vivification and Transformation.

CHAPTER XII

THE students came together in classes or small assemblies to hear and learn of the Wise Ones. The Wise Ones did not undertake to talk to the outer physical senses as I am talking to you today, but through thought-transference, that more vigorous and permeating condition which some day some of you will perceive to know and this whole nation, so largely Atlantian, will come into the full possession of. Not only could the subject intended to be taught be fully and completely received, but with more intensity and a broader wave action on the plane of intellect than you now receive.

Suppose, as has been said to you, in this day while we listened delightedly, it were possible to give to a class of students, by asking them to sit still a few moments, a demonstration of the vibrations of color, sound or other sensed vibration that lie just beyond. If I as a professor and you as a class sit listening eagerly and I say to you, "Sit still for a moment; turn inward your consciousness and perceive,"[29] then I could by the force of thought directed by my own mentality make visible to you the quiet, the peace, the harmony that always does and must attend the inner vision—how much time it would save; how much better you would remember it than now, when you have to formulate within your own brains the words symbolizing the vibrations which I poorly convey to you and which no two of you can conceive or perceive exactly alike! This was our intellectually exceptional and brilliant mental training.

Whoever was particularly bright, desirous to know of all

---

[29] Known today in the Higher Occult as Image Formation, Vivification and Transference and, when self-induced, as *Blending*. This may be made possible upon any plane of existence.

truth, whose eyes, turning to the great white tower, lifting it-self aloft above our Temple, wished within themselves that some day within its shadow they might learn more of these things, were always sure to have the opportunity. When this eventful time came and the gateway was opened wide, there came also the obligation for fulfilling even as the obligations come today.

That which a master of the later day said, "A new commandment give I unto you, that ye love one another," was the inspiration, the thought and the most intense dictum of those who taught in the Temple. There must be perfect unity, perfect harmony, perfect love for one another. Oh, that you of this latter day had never forgotten, you who have remembered and put in practice all the commandments of the "dreadful ten" concerning the physical, would only recall and practice the Eleventh. Then all that could be needed in the visible life would come.

"Seek ye first the knowledge and potency of the Unseen in the realm of Truth, and there will come to you knowledge of all else." The knowledge of the physical cannot be so very much. It lies along the contemplation of a few simple, fundamental principles. It is not so difficult to make gold as might be considered. It is not so difficult to do various other things which have come to our knowledge. Every step you have climbed along the way, which seemed so difficult at its first contemplation, after it has been accomplished, grew easier with the added knowledge.

Our records in stone, contained in the great treasury of the waters, hold embodied fundamental principles as established truths, which many earnest Souls, groping in search along the higher lines to discover, would give years of their own lives to know. Some of these, sooner or later, will come into knowledge. Those willing to advance, to expend the time necessary to make the sacrifices and take upon themselves the obligation which must rest upon the consciences of all who are admitted to participation in the truths world-wide in the scope of their action, are candidates for knowing and understanding. They will certainly advance beyond the three-fold gates into the great mysteries.

That which belonged to the Atlantians as a nation intellectually and morally was the control of all knowledge except that which belonged to the origin and power of life. This concerns the One alone.

Some of you whom I knew as men in the olden days I now perceive as women.[30] But the spirit that lies behind each one of you is the same; the perception that looks out of the eyes is the same perception that looked out of the body or dress you wore then, thousands of years ago. Oh, if you of this day and generation could only understand and perceive the treachery of the physical embrace, how the enwrapping into the physical is only a manifestation for the processes of accomplishment! If the experiences can come only through the body of a man, it takes that. If the object of the coming back into the lives can only be accomplished through the body of a woman, it accepts that with its modicum of joy and terrible burdens of pain and mad agony on all planes. The body is nothing! The Soul of the Ego is everything.

---

[30] There is nothing odd about this statement. Those who accept the Doctrine ôf Karma will know that all now on earth and who harbor the longing to be of the opposite sex rather than the sex they now bear *will be reborn as of the opposite sex*. Desire *is* the controlling law. A desire born in the present life and steadfastly adhered to throughout life becomes manifest in the next reincarnation. This naturally refers to all desires which cannot be made manifest in the present life.

CHAPTER XIII

IT WAS a doctrine of the Atlantians that the body of the physical which enwraps us is adapted to the need of the Ego holding it, as a manifestation of the processes of accomplishment. If the Ego coming back into the lives cannot accomplish its own unfolding, save through some particular experience, it compasses that particular experience if it is within its possibilities. From age to age, from generation to generation, that which stands behind all is ever the same. That which overshadows all is a part of the Divine Existence, is one with the One—a part of the Divine Existence, indivisible and always the same. This was the primary knowledge taught first in the forests amid the rocks and mountains and afterward in the Great Temple builded into these mountains. It must be remembered that very much of the work done in the Temple was accomplished by the control of the elements or elemental forces which the Brotherhood understood and exercised even in those far-off days for the lightening of the toil of the physical. This you in this day and generation have somewhat recovered. But instead of saying to the force universal, do this, you chain some portion of it and bring it under limitation of form. These limitations act for you, tirelessly toiling day and night. And so there does not come out of the surrounding conditions and vibrations the reacting powers and forces which generally tend to the physical retarding of any great building or other work of importance, because they are made up of the groans and moans of those who toil in the physical body to accomplish.

When elemental force builds it builds because of its forcefulness and there is nothing to retard. In no sense is there anything for regret or reparation. There are no tears, there are no blood marks anywhere throughout the whole work. It is clean. It is set in motion and directed by the force which originates in the potency of man the created, who thus becomes a connecting link with the potency of the One who manifested as the Universe.

In the northeastern part of the continent was a group of rocky mountains. These rocks reached far down beneath the ordinary level of the soil. They seem to have been buttressed up, apparently from the very center of the earth itself, but that it was not so appeared by the future events. But in any event they were strong enough to hold tons upon tons of piled-up rock in whatever shape it might appear.

So first the rocks were cut down to a level, and a huge plaza was thus cleared from east to west in such a fashion that both the rising and the setting sun could be seen from any part thereof. Also, the North Star and the Southern Cross, each low in the heavens, could be seen by anyone standing upon the plaza. The human view was unobstructed from horizon to horizon as far as the power of the eye could penetrate. This plaza was ample enough to hold in its confines every single member of the Atlantian nation at one time. It was many acres in extent. It is wonderful how many people can stand on one acre if they are only harmonious.

This great plaza was necessary for the Convocations and the yearly ceremonies when all the people went up to the Temple to receive guidance and instruction for the coming year. This Convocation was always at the time of the Vernal Equinox, when renewed impetus comes both to the vegetable and the animal.

Thus the mountains, partly cut down, left space also for the facade which was tunneled into for the interior of the building from the front, and to this excavation additional structures were added from time to time to meet the necessities of the Temple Colony. That is, wings were built and additional stories added, all with regard to the symmetry of the whole. The rooms and colonnades all yielded to the unification of the whole, which was the education of the Temple Staff, and through them of the whole people.

At the northeast corner, as I have already mentioned, on the foundations of solid rock, reaching far down into the earth, was builded story after story a tower. Upon this tower's top was located the tallest observatory that has ever been known in the world. There they who were wise and who were considered best, after having passed triumphantly through the intricacies, the education and unfolding of the lower degrees, kept constant ward and watch. Out of this tower, at its lower part, proceeded forth over the great area the wall of the Temple, inclosing the Great Hall of Convocation and the Temple proper; and from the Holy of Holies at the bottom of the tower Light, Strength and Force, at times of Convocation, streamed forth as the result of the united power of the Three, Five, Seven, Fifteen and Forty-five. But let us turn to a fuller description of the tower.

The tower was $22\frac{1}{2}$ feet in diameter at the highest point of the coping. It was built of hewn stone in the shape of the trunk of a tree, large at its base, growing a little smaller in diameter halfway up and then widening again.

This model from nature was considered the strongest form. The stones, as I have said, were nicely cut and laid in a peculiar cement found in the southern part of the continent, which, once hardened, was as firm as the rock itself. So the tower bore itself aloft as if it were one solid stone.

Over the top, at the distance of ten feet from the floor at the coping, was a spherical dome. It was of glass and, more than that, it was made of a single piece as transparent as water itself. Through this all the motions of the heavenly bodies could be seen and minuted from convenient points of observation in the chamber below. The floor of the hall was of mosaic, wrought in figures, and when it shall reappear he who is wise may read in this a history of the founding of the Temple, its date, its object and the purposes to which it was dedicated.

At one edge there was set in the wall a circular disc that was movable at the time of the entrance or departure for him who knew the secret spring. This was known only to the Three, one of whom was constantly on duty in attendance on the "Holy of Holies" of this Temple. There was another "Holy of Holies" in the great Hall of Convocation, but that was the symbol of the highest person of the "Superior Wisdom." One was the Superior Wisdom and the other the Inferior Wisdom. Over this floor so tessellated was spread to protect it from injury a carpet of heavy linen woven so closely that it was almost impervious to impressions from without upon it. The usual wear and tear of things earthly did not affect it in the least. This was stretched tightly upon the whole floor. Upon the upper surface of this was drawn a circle of the whole circumference of the chamber. Within this periphery were drawn three other circles which joined each other at their circumferences[31] and whose centers were each equally distant from the center of the great circle. Through these were drawn the intersecting equilateral triangles and the six-pointed star. In the center of these inscribed circles was placed a seat, one for each of the Three. In the center of the great circle was a tripod holding a censer in which burned the Eternal Fire. In their invocations, when they were reaching out to conquer new territory in the invisible, it was absolutely necessary that the potency of the Three should be embodied in the outer circle. Co-ordinate with this effort, the potency of each must guard his own particular circle, while from the center it was essential there should be wafted into space the potency which could call and

---

[31] The present insignia of the Council of Three in the Confederation of Initiates.

conquer. These were all used upon especial occasions. These vigils were nightly and daily, and the records of their observations were carefully kept. These three were wise men, for they had risen step by step from the knowledge of earthly things and their environments to a point where they could perceive all that could or would happen, not only to Atlantis, but to all the remainder of this planet.

They had also attained the point where other furnishings were not necessary for their assistance, for in the perception of the Divine Birthright they declared themselves one with the All Potency and so acted, so demanded and so perceived. This perception finally engendered pride of station, which, conjoined to their knowledge, was the cause of their overthrow.

CHAPTER XIV

IN CONSIDERING the remaining secret chambers, let us remember that all knowledge comes from the home of the Great Gods—the silence where everything is that is.

Between the station of the Three and the Five was a heavy floor of masonry, each stone of which fitted into all the others, even as one piece of solid rock is fitted into its surrounding rock. Had it all been one piece, it could not have been more lasting nor more compact. The arch of the lower chamber was like the arch of the upper chamber. From the highest concavity of the lower ceiling to the floor of the upper chamber was three and eight-tenths feet of solid masonry. The arch of the lower chamber rested upon or sprang from five pillars in the walls of the circular chamber. Between each of these a single piece of marble was set, polished to the highest possible point. One was white, one was black, one was white, one was black and one was white. Between the two white ones was a band of burnished gold, the art of preparing which, after being lost for ages, was recovered again in Etruria, whose wondrous masterpieces are the marvel and glory of the present time. It glittered and shone as only that metal can respond to the artisan's hand. These marble mirrors were turned toward the earth at a slight angle, and in them could be seen, as in the pages of an open book, all things that were happening, had happened or were about to happen. That is to say, by the art of the Wise Ones these had become reflectors of the Astral Books. Whoever knew the cipher could read, but to know the cipher they must be able to perceive, and no person could be eligible to membership in the Five who under training did not manifest this power of perception. When the love of learning and the desire for understanding had given him the first rudiments of the cipher he was transferred hither. Then, as if in a vision, he was allowed to give proof whether he could see and read. If he failed he was returned whence he came for further training, if it appeared the gift was his. If not, then only that which had happened to him was his as if he had dreamed it.

It is not necessary for me to say that the Five were rapid and accurate readers of whatever their wills sought to know. That which was good was perceived in the white mirrors. That which was evil or obstructive was seen in the black mirrors. So long as Atlantis was in its greatest power and glory, so long was the number maintained as I have described it. But during the last twenty-five years of the existence of the Temple in the city the odd mirror in the white had clouded over in a singular fashion, growing darker and darker, until the final destruction, and today under the waters there are three black and two white mirrors; but when the hour of redemption shall have struck, the stain will be wiped away from the white. Once more there will be three white and two black mirrors. In the records of the past, written on the floor of the upper chamber, there was this prophecy: "When the three are all black swift destruction cometh to the Temple and the people."

This had been well known by those whose ambition should have led to higher and better things, and although they wondered at the continuous change for the worse, so clouded had their minds become by their selfish ambitions that no notice was taken of the dreadful warning.

Although the chamber was solid and there were neither windows nor doors, there were means of ventilation by which fresh air was conveyed into and out of this apparent tomb. The means of entrance were the same as those of the upper chamber. Although no aperture communicated with the sunlight, yet apparently the light from the great dome overhead passed through the solid masonry as though it were glass. Whatever could be seen by the light in the upper chamber, with its magnificent dome of crystal, could just as easily be seen in the chamber of the Five. On the floor of this chamber also was an extremely fine mosaic record of the nation and of the Occult happenings to the same. Over this was a carpet of the same material as that above and a circle twenty-two and eight-tenths feet in diameter. Within this was drawn a pentagon, thirteen and eight-tenths feet on a side. From the center of each side of the pentagon to the point of contact with the circle, a semi-circle was drawn. In the center of the circle was a smaller circle touching all the semi-circles, four and eight-tenths feet in diameter. Where these semi-circles intersected each other were four figures resembling ellipses. At the point corresponding to the focus—the point farthest from the center— was the station of him who officiated. You will see when you draw these lines how intimately was the sustaining power of each bounded by the great circle of the environment. All were limited, supported and sustained. In the inner, the smaller circle representing with the center, the power of the One was reached and held by the semi-circle of each, and each was supported in turn by that of his brother next to him on the left and by his own power until the whole circle was completed.

Here the triangle has become the pentagon, and the symbol of the intimate relations of those who are brothers was carried out fully and completely. All the civilization the world boasts today is the result of the vibrations set in motion within this noted tower of the Atlantians.

Between the divisions of the Three and the Five were three feet of solid masonry. The roof was arched as the heavens seem to be arched, and this arch was lined with an alloy of silver, gold and copper, an alloy which the citizens of the world today would give much to be able to imitate.

It was polished to the highest degree of finish, but, strange to say, it did not reflect a single thing taking place in the chamber. It was supported in its place by seven pilasters, one of orichalcum, one of gold, one of silver, one of lead, one of tin, one of copper and one of platinum.

This was used instead of quicksilver, because the quicksilver could not be retained in place nor form, and the platinum was its opposite. On the plate of platinum at its base was engraved the proportions of the alloy used in this great concavity.

There were always sounds emanating from it. Sometimes they were sweet and harmonious, sometimes sonorous and turbulent, for it did not reflect anything within the chamber. It was a reflector of the nation's sounds and of all those with whom they had dealings. It was in touch with all the planets, and it was a curious fact that in reflecting the sounds it also reflected the colors of the sounds, because the same vibrations that make sound produce color also. So you see that in one chamber attention was called to the working of the One in the Heavens, and in the next chamber could be perceived the operations of man's thought on the Astral plane, and in the chamber of the Seven we are now about to describe the study was of the manifesting of thought in its first potency, thus in each grade approaching nearer and nearer to those to whom they ministered and who should have been their first care always and, above everything else, their supreme concern.

This chamber also, like the others, was permeated by the light which knows and recognizes no obstruction. The light was of equal volume, quality and quantity as that which lighted the uppermost chamber, and it had the same peculiarity of penetrating and giving distinct view. It pervaded the whole chamber, without having any visible source. Upon this floor also was written in mosaic, as in the other chambers, a continuance of the history and progress of the nation and the city.

Over this, too, was spread, as in the other chambers, the carpet. Upon this carpet was a circle of twenty-one feet in diameter. Within this circle was described a heptagon; to the center were drawn radii, thus making each side of the heptagon the base of a triangle of which the two radii were the other two sides. Within each of these triangles was inscribed a circle touching each of the sides. The center of these circles was the station of one of the Seven. In operating they might look to the center or the circumference or to each alternately. But whatever was done was always with the utmost harmony and unity of potency.

There is still one more chamber of potent effort; that is, the Chamber of the Fifteen. The Chamber of the Forty-five was more that of a school of training than a laboratory of Occult force. The thickness of the separating masonry was seven feet. In the center it presented a square rising above the roof of the Temple. Within it was a square room with the sides facing each of the points of the compass. Circular windows, one each, pierced the walls of the four sides. The one on the east was red, the one on the west was blue, the south was yellow and the north, white.

The floor was laid in tiles, and the tiles were of a material which generations of wear could not destroy. And upon these was a lesson which contained absolutely from beginning to end all the knowledge that man would ever need or could expect to attain upon the earth. The wisest might read it partially. To those lacking understanding, if they could decipher, it was still a mystery and foolishness.

This may seem impossible, but it is true nevertheless. When man learns that all rays come from the One, it will not be such a difficult task to find the way to the source and origin of all that mystifies and perplexes him on the earth. It is because he believes there are many and that the shadows and changing illusions are of the essence and quality of the real, that he diffuses his power and baffles his own inquiries.

In this chamber in a semi-ellipse were fifteen seats, seven on each side of the keystone of the arch. The roof was also square. In one of the foci was a crystal globe from which light always emanated. In the hours of rest it was necessary. In the hours of day, light from the outer permeated the room. The crystal globe hung midway from floor to ceiling without visible support, swaying gently with the movements of the thought-currents about it. In the other focus of this semi-ellipse three brazen serpents, supported on their tails and rearing upward, held aloft in their mouths a censer in which burned the perpetual fire.

During the time of sessions, incense and perfumes fed by invisible hands brought peculiar effects to those waiting for instruction and guidance. It was here those who were fitted, after training in the school of the Forty-five and waiting, were selected for admission under obligation for further training and practice. If they kept their obligation they then might some time hope for promotion.

If they did not keep their obligation, then they fell back. There was always more or less change going on in this chamber of trial. From these Fifteen culled from the whole nation came the Seven, Five and Three.[32] Nor were they allowed to know of the powers beyond them, except they occupied the chair of the Elder Brother who was their appointed leader and guide.

They came and went amongst the people and were considered as persons of authority amongst the Temple Dwellers. They were but little removed from the forces lying below them, which they utterly and entirely controlled for the purpose of

---

[32] The method pursued at this day except that, as already mentioned, the Councils are now the Three, Seven and Nine, the Council of Five, because of its vibratory weakness, having been eliminated.

massing and using them for concentrated power.

This chamber rested upon the massive walls of the Forty-five by a ponderous arch whose spherical edges met the solid rock, the buttressed foundation of the world, seemingly uplifted for the very purpose of this support.

Beneath the floor of the chamber of the Forty-five was hewn out the "Holy of Holies" of the Great Hall of Convocation, so that the mysteries intended and desired to be communicated could be made manifest to the people at the stated times and seasons. This was the ultimate outcome of all this interlinking of organization.

The chamber of the Forty-five was twenty-five by twenty-five feet, and the walls were twelve feet thick. Within this wall, impervious to sound or impression from without, the students of this degree met. The chamber was so arranged, with its lofty, arched roof and solid floor of finest woods brought from all quarters of the earth, that the conditions of pure air were fully met. They who were sitting, sometimes for a shorter time, sometimes for days that seemed but hours, listened enchantedly to that which was propounded to them. There was no lack of understanding from crudeness or from any disarrangement of the physical conditions of harmony and peace, which all men must have to be at the highest point of perception.

CHAPTER XV

THUS sitting, the Forty-five were arranged in four rows of seats, eleven in each row, arranged elliptically, facing a raised dais on which sat the Elder Brother during the hours of instruction. The rows of seats were raised one behind the other and thus gave perfect and unobstructed liberty of sight and perception to the Brothers who sat upon them in the order of their ages. There was always close to the seat of the Elder Brother another seat, and this, empty always to personal sense, to those who could see on the psychic plane was filled by an Elder Brother from the Invisible, as a mentor and guide, as an influencer of the Elder Brother of the visible, to receive whatever might be given either from his own knowledge or by his coming in touch more readily with the invisible, thus receiving out of the realms of the Invisible that which was needed for instruction on any and all of the mortal-touched planes.

A narrow staircase was arranged in the thick wall, which led to the chamber of the Forty-five, and a sliding door, opening to the lightest touch of those who knew, admitted into the chamber. This chamber was ceiled and floored, sides, top and bottom, with wood they obtained from the country to be known in the later days as South America, but then a large island. It was of a peculiar hardness, dark red in color and susceptible of the most brilliant and lasting polish. It was so well fitted together that it seemed like one piece. They who were the builders controlled the elemental force which was able to do persistently and in the finest manner whatever it was set to do. So when the door was closed it appeared as if they were in a shell from which there was no possible escape. There was no danger from any outer accident, except possibly an earthquake. But for many hundred years no earthquake had occurred. For many years to come none was predicted by even the wisest astrologers of the Temple. The doorway by which they entered was in the open end of the oval upon which the seats were placed. Within the whole chamber, at distances far enough to protect the sight of those who were receiving instruction from any bewilderment by the light, points of emanating brilliancy were placed. What these points of light were composed of, hundreds of men in the days to come will give several years of their lives to know and never be able to find out.

Before these facts shall have again come into the possession of men, there will have been those who will have come to the place where their hands have laid almost upon the thing they crave and so covet. These lights, held as it were by invisible torch-bearers, could be perfectly stationary for any length of time, or they could be moved as there was necessity for concentrating or diffusing that which they gave forth.

At times, in full view of the whole number, would come up something acting as a reflector of thought action and picturing either the Past or the Future. This great transparent blackboard, so to speak, so you may understand just what I am trying to say, held itself in place or seemed to dissolve under the will of those who were instructing, and while one could see through it, it was an impermeable barrier to any passage through it; no thick bar of brass could more stoutly resist. While there was nothing of it that appealed to the sense of sight, there was still such force that it served as an obstruction, although invisible, upon this clear sheet, of size large enough to fill the whole twenty-five feet, rising up as might be necessary for the accommodation of whatever was thrown upon it, out of the mental conditions of those who taught under the law set up by those who in the highest Chamber of the Temple watched and waited through the centuries. So in the times of instruction the Elder Brother detailed whatsoever should come to him out of his own mentality or should be given him out of the records of the past or out of that which should be the result of sequence in the Future. At the same time he demonstrated upon this invisible screen exactly as he described, both as to what had already occurred or might take place. Did he desire to unfold a line of sequence, then as he talked of the sequence in a particular way the whole company would see that all the sequences were alike; that everything moved forward on the line of the One Creative Thought in perfect harmony for accomplishment of all events in manifestation. The things that seemed to happen were due to the perception of the investigator and to the non-manifestation at the same time of the peculiarities appearing in the individual through which cognizance was made.

But let us describe one session: Minute by minute, there have been persons coming through the door into the chamber, which is held in the softness of a dim, pleasant twilight, not clear enough for perception except at close range. They have quietly and without speaking come forward each to the seats where they have evidently been assigned, then, sitting, have restfully waited in silence and peace. In coming in, they have all advanced from the door of entrance across the space where the square of demonstration was held, thus showing as they came in there was nothing between them and their seats.

They have passed on and all are now seated. There was not a single absentee. Such a thing as absenteeism or tardiness in the workings of the Great Temple was unknown. Too well they knew the wonderful power of CONTINUOUS, UNBROKEN ACTION.[33] The hour strikes from a sonorously toned bell, seem-

---

[33] A vitally important lesson yet to be learned and fully comprehended by present-day Neophytes and Candidates for seats at the Council table. No position on earth, no opportunity, business, honor or benefit, can possibly be of value to one honored to sit with the Council.

ingly in the center of the room. To the personal sense, no bell
is visible. It might seem strange that we Atlantians had any
idea of measuring time, but it must be remembered there is
nothing not known; nothing that will ever be known; nothing
that the world will ever receive that was not received by those
who, eager for knowledge, were not only eager to understand but to use. We had perceived and received all human
knowledge.

As the hour strikes in the manner I have described, the
Forty-four and the Elder Brother, looking up, perceived a
form dim and misty in outline has filled the chair of the pre-
siding instructor. Sitting in the position of meditation, which
in the later times the Egyptians copied in their Temple work
and left us on record on their books of stone, they concentrate
on the thought of unity.

There were three points upon which they concentrated in
succession: Unity, Harmony and Love, for these three constitute the Unmanifested, so they who were in the Forty-five
were taught. When the quickening of the Invisible within
themselves had become exalted, at a sign from the Elder
Brother they stood and, making a sign that is recognized by
both the Visible and the Invisible, repeated words having of
themselves potency, force and intense harmonious vibration.
These words were reinforced by other vibrations resembling
the rolling sound of a great organ. It was a reverberation,
partly reflected and partly responsive, out of the Invisible by
which they received answer and thus became unified into the

Therefore, it would be well for such to recognize the vital importance
of setting aside, for the time being, all other affairs, wholly forgetting
them, in order that they may in heart and Soul partake of the vibratory
forces which will descend upon them as they are seated at the table in
the Council. By these means may they reap all those spiritual powers
and forces which are unobtainable by any other means or in any other
manner. For such honor have men labored and suffered through many
centuries, and it is only as they forget all else that they may reap the
harvest the Soul has sown.

sense and condition of desire in its most perfect form for whatever might and could be given them. On this night of which I
am speaking the Elder Brother commenced describing the possibilities of unfolding in all who were present; of the unfolding
of the earth's condition; of the things that would bear down
in the way of clouds and darkness; of limitation, obstruction
and opposition; and as he described, step by step, that which
might come under certain circumstances, the screen of almost
invisible material quivered and shimmered with the lights and
shades passing over it. To those who perceived with only the
physical eye, there was only a dancing of lurid fires. To each
who had come into more perfect condition, it was possible to
perceive not only the play of the light, but the varying colors
and forms which lay behind the colors, not only upon the pictures of the scenes, but upon the scenes themselves. The
Future presented itself as the Eternal Now. One of the Forty-
five, looking forward, not dreaming that all that seemed to occur was about to come in the close Future, hardly attempting
to estimate time, saw then how the Brotherhood of Wisdom,
for the Ages, might find itself for a time unrepresented upon
the earth; but, under the obligations which make the members
of the Brotherhood acting, living members, whether living or
dead, so the membership in the invisible sought, desired and·
brought about the remanifestation and rehabilitation. All the
signs and points made and desired to be emphasized were illustrated upon our screen. And thus, as the time went on, in that
which was to be the dawn of a new recreation, so to speak, we
perceived certain gatherings of the far Future were also being
pictured upon the screen. I remember it all well, for it seemed,
as the memory comes to me out of the Past, there was some
responding condition within myself; not only did I see it and
feel it, as regarding myself, but that others would then come
into it at that time whose presence and help would recall the
now, but to be known then as ancient days, and they would

testify to the truth of the then pictured.

I cannot tell you fully of all the drapings and decorations and precious metals that adorned this chamber, but you may imagine for yourselves nothing was spared to make it a fit place, both in the conditions of the Visible and in the potencies of the Invisible, drawn from all over the world for the inculcating in its fullest and its strongest the truth of that which will be fully verified. They who now in life know not only of the lower, but also of the higher, thus perceive the apparently futile in many respects has for its governing, impelling force the strength and power of the ages behind it. All move on to fulfill in the completed outline whatever was set and designed to be accomplished.

Thus the lessons given to the Forty-five were either in voiced vibration, through the sense of sight or by thought transference. Whichever method was used, the vibrations made themselves plainly visible to the sense to which they were addressed. Their vividness depended upon the intensity with which the thought was projected. But at all times during a session of the Forty-five there were shadows more or less distinct in outline, playing over this wonderful spectrum.

When instructions were being received from the Three the play of forms and colors were something that has never been seen elsewhere in the whole world. The reflections then obtained have really so impinged upon the Great Astral Record that the works accomplished have become mighty influences upon the Globe. The record of what these denizens of the secret chambers of the Great Temple thought and did is one day to become supremely dominant in the affairs of the world. As the cycle rises to completion it will become more and more potent. He who is wise and able has thus given some outline.

CHAPTER XVI

I HAVE tried thus far to give you a description of the Great Temple of Atlantis and of the Tower that was one of the wonders of the world. That which was in sight was not by any means all; even as the tree, bearing fruit after its kind above the earth, is by no means the largest nor most important part of the organic development. The organs of growth and transmutation are hidden from the curious eyes of the idle. So we have in the mid-heavens the angels and spirits of light;[34] on earth, mortals both visible and invisible; beneath the earth's surface are the beings belonging to the lower races who have never been subjugated by the spiritual powers of such as held sway in the upper chambers.

These elemental beings will be classed in the later day as Salamanders, Water Spirits, Kobolds, Goblins and Dwarfs. They are workers in the Fire, the Water and the Earth or Rocks. It was in the internal fires of unregisterable heat that during the latter days of Atlantis the immense stores of gold and jewels which the Temple Treasury held were manufactured under PRIMAL CONDITIONS. In this also was illustrated the great law of Transmutation.

As the Great Tower flung itself toward the mid-heavens, pointing everlastingly upward, it indicated the constant search man is making to the extent of his ability for truth, light and potency. The part of the Tower that sank lower and lower into the bowels of the Earth typified the material and physical

---

[34] These are known in the Occult as the Hierarchies, and it is the privilege of the truly faithful Atlantian earth-born to come into touch with these Principalities of Light. So simple are the instructions and the means that their vital importance is frequently lost sight of by the Neophyte who enters upon his second section of the study and training.

uses of that which was capable of transmutation. It also held within itself the lesson of the "Descent into Matter"—man's environments. So far as man himself was concerned, it held also the doctrine of the Three Brains. To all the world, both Atlantian and foreign, the lesson was: "In the heavens above and the earth beneath, and the waters under the earth."

It has already been said that the whole city of Atlantis was arrayed in a splendor whose glory was never equaled. Its buildings have never been surpassed either in the symmetry of their architecture, in the material used or in the tastefulness of its preparation and artistic designs. There was also a marvelous exhibition of gold and jewels in a profuseness carried up to the verge of the barbaric.

These means for personal adornment were also used by all the people, even those in the humble walks of life, if Atlantis could be said to have had any such. The relations of poverty and riches long since had ceased to press on the attention of the nation. It was evident in the latter days that some source of almost limitless supply must be easily accessible. The Tower, which lifted proudly its head on high, went down into the mountains the same distance, and the cellars and sub-cellars were occupied by beings who belonged to the lower races who had been subjugated by the spiritual powers of those who held sway in the upper chambers.

None of the uninitiated knew for a certainty of that which was going on within the mountain. Only to the Three was this knowledge fully confided by the Builders.[35] To them, long ago all material things which are deemed of any value by mortals or of any use or importance whatever had ceased to be of

---

[35] Only the Council of Three today can know the inner and secret workings of the August Fraternity, because these are chosen from among those who have attained to the *Exalted Third,* and frequently these are so unassuming and silent that they are considered the least among the Initiates.

consequence, only so far as they might adorn or make beautiful either the Temple or the City.

Underneath the Sanctuary, entered by a door opening into the solid rock at the rear, was a flight of stairs leading down into a chamber hewn out of the rock. Out of this another staircase led into a similar chamber, and still another and another, and yet another staircase and chamber.

Within these chambers were curious implements, fashioned for use in the operations of the workers. These operations required the use of certain materials to make the manifesting and finishing of their work more easy. Their projected spirit power brought back the results produced by the various combinations. Many of these implements and operations will come into the hands of the reincarnated Atlantians from time to time, and more of them will not be given out except into the hands of the most trusted few.

In the First Cellar, Spirits of the Air labored and toiled, doing the will of the Masters.

In the Second Cellar the Spirits of the Earth moved to and fro, intent on carrying out that to which they were set.

In the Third Cellar, Elementals whose forms but thinly clothed the fierce, blazing fires within solved the varying problems of metallurgy.

In the Fourth Cellar, the lowest of all, the Spirits of the great, watery deep, fashioned whatever man needs and lays hold upon from their realm, either for use or adornment.

Vast tunnels led into the interior of the mountains and the continent from each of these cellars. The spirits of the air, by a spiral course, ascended to the highest points of the mountains and here communicated with their fellows in the outer world, receiving supplies.

The tunnel from the Cellar of the Earth Spirits opened into

an inaccessible part of the mountain, on a little plateau, which was constantly guarded by an impenetrable veil of fog.

The tunnel of the Fire Spirits led under the continent, diagonally down to the volcanic fires of the earth.

The tunnel of the Water Spirits communicated directly with the seas by the shortest feasible route.

In the center of the mountain was a cave-like room, which was the Treasury of the Temple. This storehouse communicated with all four of the tunnels and by a secret entrance with the Temple itself. It was not only the Treasury of the Temple, but of the nation as well.

He who knew the secret of the Treasury would stand in the rear of the Most Holy Place at the hour of high noon on a certain day of the year and watch until, by a peculiar arrangement of the polished marbles, a single ray of sunlight thrown from the chambers above would be reflected upon the wall at the back. This could only be seen when the observer was in a particular position and then but for a period of three minutes. Having perceived this, he would turn one-quarter to the right and move seven steps in a straight line, then, turning to his original position, he took five steps more and then, turning one-quarter to the left, three steps brought him to an apparently blank wall, highly ornamented. But to him who had the key a slight pressure on a jewel of immense value, apparently placed there for ornamentation, opened a huge door of rock weighing tons, but so balanced that it moved easily and without noise and was screened from view by the shrine which stood in front. Entering boldly, as soon as he stepped upon the flagging inside the door, the great stone settled back into its first position. It could be opened on the inside by pressing upon a slight projection at the back. Thirteen times thirteen steps brought him again to a blank wall, through a high, arched passage lighted by the never-dying lights produced by the action of positive and negative earths combined with the rock which gave out an electrical phosphorescent light, the secret of which perished with the nation, but which may be recovered at a later day by the chemists, as those who are expert in safes recover the forgotten combination of the locks thereof. Once more he who knew the secret spring might open and pass within. The Treasure Chamber opened to the Temple Inspector on the day of the Vernal Equinox when the sun went down in the West.

CHAPTER XVII

I T WAS a sight that met his gaze which an avarice-tainted Soul would never be allowed to contemplate. Great heaps of gold, silver and aluminum, the method used by us for obtaining which was the result of condensed electrical power, acting through surcharged magnets of the finest steel. In the times to come the forces of induction will for a time be very little understood. But the day will come when they will have the very best method of extracting aluminum from the original clay as their secret. These stacked-up heaps of the noble metals were in quantity sufficient to last for centuries, nor had their continuous production ceased, but every day added to the increasing store.

Beside these were heaps upon heaps of priceless jewels, some of them still warm from the fires of earth and water in which they were crystallized. Both the polished and the uncut glittered and shone here in the light, which was as full and strong as in the passage-way.

Here the workers in the various cellars deposited the results of their labors. From here the civil rulers received whatever they needed, upon sudden pressure, in their traffic with all outside nations of the earth. But there were also in the city their own storehouses and treasuries of wealth. This was only that which belonged to the Temple and was the result of the labors of the servants of the Temple. In case of necessity the civil rulers could draw upon the Temple for reserves in any amount.

No human eye hath seen nor any tongue described the immensity of the wealth lying to this day in that strong mountain treasury beneath the waves. There is enough gold lying in it to destroy the value of the gold now in use upon the earth. But when the day of its discovery shall come it will belong to a nation who shall have so purified itself from avarice that there shall be no Karmic weight transferred from this treasure to the shoulders of its finders.

Upon the inner door that opens into this treasury rests a seal. Upon this seal is the following inscription: "The potent Will of the Most Mighty holds this treasure safely until the time of the restoration shall come. The Angel of the waters has charge of it."

It seems hardly necessary to say that the jewels and gold were all manufactured by the occupants of the cellars and that it was the reflection out of the Astral light on the vision of the clear-sighted that made so many earnest believers in the transmutation of base metals into gold and jewels.

CHAPTER XVIII

THE manner of adjustment and Convocation was after the following fashion: As has already been stated, the priesthood had charge of the education of the people. There were some better fitted for one thing than another, as even at the present day. But those who were especially gifted with understanding, who combined reverence with intense desire for the knowledge of that which was unseen and hidden, wherever found, were transferred to the Temple service, and this was the first step in the separation of the wheat from the chaff.

Those who in their training, as part of the Temple family, exhibited a still higher degree of intelligence and perception were again set aside for the Forty-five and again in the same manner for the Fifteen. The selection for the higher chambers followed in the same order from those best developed and adapted to the work to be done. The training of the Forty-five was, first, submission to unseen guidance in a more intense degree than as ordinary scholars of the Temple. When they had reached the point where, because they were asked, they took pains to think out along any line that ought or might be desired, their power for broad, intense contemplation had increased until their meditations had become second nature.

The next step was concentration. Notice the steps: *submission, meditation, concentration.* When the thought was well massed and the vibrations were uniform and persistent, then they were taught to project the concentered thought which had been the essence of their meditations. As the absolute Unity, IT meditates, as the Divine Ideation; It concentrates as the Creative Thought; It projects. So nearly as the Earth-dweller may follow this line of procedure, so nearly will he be able to lay hold of the Unseen force and make it available for all good purposes.

Years of discipline in the Forty-five and still later in the Fifteen made each member of the Seven ready and expert in these labors. The perfection was carried still farther in the Five, where they practiced the attracting of the vibrations of unseen force of any kind whatever into alignment with their own projection, thus controlling the powers of the great names.

It was as if workmen, taking a ball of soft metal from the crucible or furnace, should whirl it rapidly in the air until it had assumed a certain form and then launch it forth to fulfill their will.

But to the Three belonged the directing of all the force thus gathered. Nor was there allowed to be any chance for mistake, not even a clashing thought in the minds of the Three. It was always determined, by the casting of lots, who should control the outward moving of the vibrations at any Convocation, and to the power of the one of the Three the other two added their potency. The regular Convocations were under the Full Moon of each month. But the special Convocations were under the will of the Three. When special Convocation was desired the word given at the last Convocation was whispered to each, out of the Invisible, in such a manner that all could recognize and understand the call.

At the close of the Convocation the Elder Brother of each Section received from the Elder Brother of the highest Section a word like this: "Myld." This the Elder Brother communicated to the inner sense of the instructed (it never being spoken aloud) as the closing password of the session.

If there were a special Convocation, then to each one came out of the Silence the Word to the inner ear, and thereby not only was the day named, but the hour was fixed, being always at a certain distance from the Sun's setting. If there were no special Convocation, then at the next regular meeting each one present at the opening, in succession, in low breath pronounced the given word so that which had been given out was again recalled.

The work was formally opened in the upper Chamber by the Three. At the first word of invocation, the "Center of Fire"[36] glowed and flashed, and whatever had been planned or arranged for needing potency was apportioned amongst the lower chambers. In the chamber of the Five the polished marble slabs reflected the orders. In the chamber of the Seven the notes of the bell, like the tones of some sweet harmony, told the story. But to the trained inner ear of the Elder Brother in the Fifteen, as by inspiration came that which was necessary to be done.

There was no hesitation in compliance, no timidity in obedience and no delay in action. The gathered force of the whole nation in charge of the Forty-five was sent forward to the Fifteen and there, as intensified, was passed on to the Seven, where, bound together, solidified and shaped, the projected potency was again handed on to the Five, who harmonized the activity of the potent vibrations with the vibrations of the Universe. Thus changed from the Special to the Universal, it was placed in the hands of the Three who, uniting their force in the One, stood ready to hurl into space, in all the awfulness of power, this projection of the concentrated potency of a nation by which they could really expect to hold and keep everything they had seized upon.

The matter of training cannot be understood from mere description. Only when students attempt of themselves to bring

---

[36] Not an earthly or material fire, but the Fire or Light which is gradually brought into manifestation and vivification by means of what is known in the Higher Occult as the *Fire and Light Arcanum Drill*, the potency of which is so great, when fully developed, it can create or destroy worlds, yet so simple that a child is able to practice it.

their mental conditions under subjugation can be understood how long it takes to accomplish the wonderful things done by our Ancient Brothers.

CHAPTER XIX

THEY who ruled in Atlantis, as the priesthood, were successful in guiding the ship of State wisely and fortunately so long as they considered the interests of the whole nation as one. As long as they put aside the sense of separateness, while they only sought for wisdom, that the benefit growing out of it might be utilized in common by all the nation who looked for light and guidance from them, all was well. As long as the Three, Five and Seven, with the Fifteen and Forty-five, were separate and yet one,[37] the only distinction being to see who could best work with the highest potency in the position where he was placed, satisfied that the well and perfect doing and the acquiring of knowledge from experience would bring the reward that comes always to attainment.

They looked to the perfect doing and not to the result, and out of this desire grew the concentration of potency in their hands which made them the one nation of the earth exceeding all others in the unraveling of the hidden mysteries. But it was not a task of idle floating, but sometimes of fierce, desperate warfare in the domains of the Invisible. As one point after another unfolded to their perceptions, those who held guard over the hidden truths or those who wrought ignorantly or malevolently to confuse mortal understanding used every effort to upset and, if it were possible, to cut off the keys of the Universal principles. And it was many years, aye, centuries, before they had compassed the fact that numbers harmoniously united and agreed upon a certain single point on

---

[37] The operating Law of Unity in diversity. The power of the many manifesting as, or through, one. The concentration of all forces by all men, on a single objective. Many minds with but a single thought-desire.

spiritual lines were just as powerful as the combinations on the physical plane, with the difference that if spiritual conditions were once perfectly trained and harmonized, there could be no defection nor sudden weakness, for weakness is in no sense a spiritual attribute, while an army or other mass of physical conditions might at any time be stampeded.

Therefore, in all the work none were admitted to the separate and secret assemblies until the overcoming of the body and its desires was far advanced, thus leaving the Spirit a clear field in which to operate.

Another point: as soon as the Occult ideas and thoughts were strongly developed, it served as a magnet for those who were in or on the same lines of thought, both from the incarnating spheres and also from other points upon the earth where lamps lighted from the Atlantian torch by its inspiring reflection had stimulated those who came within its reach to a higher and more vigorous search. Knowing of Atlantis, they gravitated thither, and here they would have remained and shared with Atlantis the fate that overtook her, blotting out for a time from the earth all the knowledge that went before, had not those who in the Silence of the Unseen, watched and foreseen the cataclysm (but not its cause), worked to scatter abroad upon the earth enough to become the seed and salt of salvation for the generations that have followed.

In all the movements of the earlier day the segregation and massing unavoidably led to the pressing forward to the front upon the development along the new lines of someone who could become under inspiration a leader. This was all well, except as the world always resents and resists the aggressiveness of new ideas with the knife, the fagot, the scaffold and in later days with the subtler force of mind, thus crushing, torturing and destroying the instruments or leaders.

They who were the depositories of knowledge for the time

being thus suffered ignominious death. The knowledge itself has been in great danger from the machinations of secret enemies, of total eradication from the earth and the perceptions of its inhabitants. This was likely to happen before its firm establishment could be accomplished. This fact was well known and understood by the malign forces. Upon this knowledge they acted again and again, seeking to have the leaders in Occult movements either bring destruction upon themselves or have others entirely cut them off.

Therefore, those having this matter in charge have resolved, instead of teaching men through the tongue and brain of a Brahma or a Jesus, His place should be supplied by a sodality of many welded into one. But even here they stand face to face with another obstacle. It has been an essential that, if the truth be preserved, individuality must increase in its perception and reality, and in the latter days they will be confronted with the intense individuality of the people who are confused and overcome by the sense of separateness. They who seek to study on these lines and to gain wisdom must, as it were, train the units made up of members into a oneness or individuality of the whole, and thus shall be born a new MESSIAH or a new Truth. The *Christos* of that Great Cycle will be a union of many individuals[38] or a nation who shall stand as the representatives of the new unfoldment of Truth.

In the Record of the Adepts there is a vision described as seen by one of the Mighty Ones; of an image whose head, body and limbs were made up of different metals, and the feet were of iron and aluminum. Each of these metals represented a

---

[38] Just as Jesus who became the Christ was the messiah or teacher of the first century, so will oneness or individuality in the present age manifest as *Manisis*, the *complete* one, the personification of individualized responsibility. This Age is *now*, the nation chosen in the dark past is America—that land spoken of by Isaiah, overshadowed by wings —the wings of the Eagle.

Messianic age, a new Truth and an Empire directly relating to some manifestation of that truth. These will represent the leaders of the previous dispensations, and then follows the vision, a stone cut out of the mountain without hands, which represents a nation fashioning itself until it shall have obtained MESSIAHSHIP, and thus, more powerful, it shall overshadow in its manifestation and dispensation all that has come before. All who are looking toward the light, ALL who are seeking unselfishly for wisdom, must, as constituent parts of that nation, attain such light, such wisdom; and, drawing closer and closer together, like drops of mercury, when they touch they shall become as one. For this we work and wait.

CHAPTER XX

AMONG the archives of that time and country has come to the knowledge of our present generation the following prophecy:

And it shall come to pass in those days in which the highest knowledge that has ever been given to the world shall be seized upon by the few and, if rightfully and truthfully held for the many, will bring to all those who shall come upon the earth wisdom, blessing and growth. But there must also be an overcoming of the natural and physical which will bring disturbance and sore distress, because the physical yields not to the rule of the Spirit without much resistance. All progress in the Soul's career is stimulated by the instinct of the Spirit to return to the condition of its first powers and estate before it should have individualized itself from the ONE. It is no sin or crime to seek to know by all the means within the power of the Spirit to grasp or undertake. Nor does the ONE resent as sin such attempts. On the contrary, IT intends that they who have become individualized shall sooner or later enter into all knowledge. That is the perfect attainment. It shall come to pass, whoever fits the self for knowledge shall receive it, but whoever attempts to grasp potency without being fitted to handle it, serious consequences will ensue, and the thing already attained may be taken away. There can be no sin for those who shall have knowledge in the grasping of the very highest in their pursuit; *but if they shall seek, before they have made themselves ready, to grasp that which is withheld simply by their* OWN FORCE OF POTENCY, *disregarding the consenting or the law of the ONE, then there will come dire results.* Or if it so happen that the nation shall have so far advanced that their knowledge would be dangerous to the other nations of the world in its use, then will it be withdrawn. But this is true, that the physical man is of no value, only as an agent in the computation of the happenings upon the earth. While it might seem to man an awful thing that millions of bodies should cease to exist, there was nothing in that issue that could be charged against the leaders. That was something distinct by itself and something that fulfilled the law. The thing for which the leaders suffered was disobedience of the law which denied to the created the forceful taking from the ONE any knowledge for which the taker is not prepared.

When limited power meets Universal potency, there can be but one issue. So now understand: there was no sin, but simply the outcome of the law of the Universe. Even the intense desire, which might seem a sin, was in one sense lawful and the result of causes implanted by the Creative Thought itself. They were not responsible, but they were the instruments. It was necessary that the law should be proved. It has always been a saying of the Wise Ones that those things which seem to be great disasters to the earth-dwellers must come to pass, and instruments must be used for that purpose. But these instruments standing in the front must suffer for that which they have provoked.

As to the outlook for accomplishment, the instruments of the mighty forces of the Unseen evidently have not developed the strength we desire nor that is necessary for the perfect culmination. Until further training can develop proper concentration, they seek to bridge over and to hold as much as possible of that which has already been gained.

EPILOGUE

THE SINKING OF ATLANTIS AND ITS SIXTY-FOUR MILLION INHABITANTS

"BY THE *silent forces of the conscious Souls of the Masters,* the people of Atlantis had been lifted grade by grade as rapidly as they could assimilate the instructions which are of so much influence and assistance in the duties and pleasures of life. Just as fast as they could be educated to perceive these facts, they were advanced in the scale of existence.

"It is true of all peoples, nations, kindreds and tongues that, in proportion as the lower classes rise from a given starting point toward the Light, the force generated (vibrations set in motion) by their action will lift those who are sensitive and fit still farther above them.[39] It is better to be the wise men of a nation of philosophers than the learned of a race of cringing slaves.

"It is not strange, therefore, that these of whom I speak should have held the mightiest secrets of the universe in their keeping. It was not strange that the trackless wastes of water in unknown seas became to them familiar paths, nor that the mysteries of the earth, of the air and of all Nature were at their command. The archives of all ancient nations, carved in

---

[39] The most powerful argument against the doctrine and practice of Collectivism by a people or nation and *for the encouragement* of individualism. The mass can *never* be raised *en masse.* It is only as individuals with high and powerful incentives raise themselves above the common lot, either through achievement or possessions, that they become shining lights, incentives, for others and arouse in them a desire to be, or to possess, like those who have advanced, and this acts as an urge for them to try. Where none are raised to honors above their fellow-men, there is no incentive to be other than of the herd, and the entire mass gradually becomes inert and retrogrades.

their books of stone, speak clearly and truly of them. In Egypt, in Assyria, in India, are found the same inscriptions, conveying the same knowledge that is today locked up in the ruined cities covered by the forests of thousands of years in Yucatan.

"The western lamp of knowledge was ever lighted from the east. From the proud seagirt continent of Atlantis went forth, as from the sun, to all parts of the earth under the heavens, the Illumination of truth and knowledge.

"The old Atlantians, going forth in their galleys hither and yon, so controlled the Elementals by their knowledge of the Hidden Laws of Nature that they had no need to wait for the moving of the winds nor tides. Like *Christos*, who in the storm stilled the waves and bade them be at peace, and immediately they were at the place whither they were going, so the Atlantians moved over the wide wilderness of waters on the earth, scattering the seeds of their knowledge along the shores they visited. The seeds fell into good ground in Egypt, Chaldea and India.

"It can be noted wherever the pressure of the ever-recurring demands of the physical—that never-yielding circle of necessity—was least on the matter over which the spirit sought to maintain dominion, meanwhile sinking deeper and deeper into its illusions with the downward rush of the cycle, there the seeds of Truth took root and grew most vigorously. At such points were more leisure, strength and purpose to bring forth as fruit the knowledge of the unseen in its greatest perfection and abundance. Spirit dominion is a tropical fruit reaching mature perfection quickest in those countries where the bountiful earth ministers voluntarily, always anticipating man's physical necessities. *Sun-cooked food does not stimulate groveling desires.*

"The dwellers in more rigorous latitudes who, in spite of opposing force, still gain spiritual elevation for themselves are richer in strength and force. *This is the result of the discipline acquired in the overcoming of the natural obstacles of their environment.*[40] *The harder the battle, the more important the victory.* So long as Atlantis obeyed the law that makes all men gods in wisdom, it prospered mightily. But there came at last a time when they who had the knowledge only in trust permitted themselves to think, to wish and to plan for grasping the *absolute control of the whole world.* In this they sought to climb into the seat and place of the Supreme. *Beyond the earth lies only the universe. The lesser is but the result of the greater.*

"The One denies no one knowledge. Whoever seeks to take from it its authority, its supremacy, thus attempting arrogation or absorption into the Oneness *in any other than the appointed ways which lie open to all created beings, shows a taint of grossness inspiring the desire surely provocative of swift destruction.* They who had thus planned were powerful far beyond the conception of the mortal, holding at their option all the secrets of Nature save one, that one embracing the Infinite supremacy of the *One.*

"These leaders had freely scattered knowledge abroad upon the earth. By *self-denial* and *long training* they had attained; and yet at almost the supreme moment, dazzled by the brightness of the Illumination, they looked once again toward self. From their memories faded out the unchanging law: '*Thus far and no farther, mayst thou go.*' The ceaseless breaking of the

---

[40] The more opposition there is, the greater the strength and power gained in the overcoming. Every victory over environments and circumstances adds strength for still greater achievements. Man should not seek the undesirable merely to test his strength—that is challenging fate, but he should cheerfully accept the battle which confronts him, and once he fully comprehends the Law he no longer bemoans his fate when the unpleasant appears, but right willingly enters into the fray in the same spirit the football player enters the gridiron against what appears to be overwhelming odds. It is the *spirit,* as much as the battle, which brings the victory.

waves of the mighty sea against the silent resistance of rock-bound coasts ceased to utter its warning to dazed mentality. The oncoming day, beginning of the end to those who had forgotten the very life and essence of the One, was at hand. The proud city of Atlantis, city and continent one, sitting as a queen upon the throne of the waters, had, by arrogant presumption, filled full the cup of wrath for which expiation must be made. They—masters of all the Elements and all lawful knowledge of the Unseen—now sought the *forbidden*, as if the part should demand equality with the whole. Step by step they had reached the veil separating them from the whiteness of the *Immediate Presence;* and now, as the last *fatal* step, they had determined by the exercise of their most potent skill to rend the veil and come unheralded and unsummoned before the face of IT whom no man hath seen at any time.[41]

"Carefully were their preparations made; most accurately were the sacred computations wrought out to decide the auspicious hour. . . . Panoplied with the consciousness of *previous* achievement, their call to the embattled hosts of the universe rang out along the astral currents. Confidently the word of power was spoken in all the pride of *human* will. The expected accomplishment did not follow. To their amazed horror, they discerned a new vibration, a resultant of creative thought in *its own defense*. To this they had no key, and, first bewildered, then terrified, they perceived that the immense

---

[41] "No man shall see God face to face (in person) and live." *That is the irrevocable law.* He who attempts to rend the veil destroys himself. God *can* be seen, but *only* through the Light which *reflects* him. Man may come face to face with God, but only through the *finding* of the *Ineffable Light* within himself. All men have the privilege to seek for and find this Light and to recognize God therein. The August Fraternity has achievement constantly in view, and the aim and end of the training, of Soul Development and Illumination, is to bring this Light into manifestation. There is but *one* way, a method taught for the past many centuries, and known only to the Arcane Priesthood. During a million years there has been no change in the method, nor will there be in a million years to come. It is *the* Way; it is the *only* Way.

force momentarily *unbound by their own act* had *destroyed the accurate balance and adjustment of Nature's laws.* Utterly without resource, they waited for the outcome.

"Thus knowing the *inner,* behold the outer. The sun rises in its eastern splendor. The mighty millions who dwell in palaces and temples, in luxury and frugality, dream not of nor can they understand the word of the Omnipotent, already spoken and gone forth whereunto it was sent. They awake to their life of ease and pleasure with the self-assurance that the thing existing hitherto will still continue to be. In their hearts they say: 'Have we not compelling power and force? Sufficient for the day is the evil thereof.' They pass on, without concern, to their usual affairs. Clouds begin to interrupt the clearness of the sky. They deepen and darken. The uncontrollable, elemental storm of the tropics, after years of durance, has burst its prisoning fetters. The people are awed by the terrific intensity of the outburst, but comfort their hearts with the idea that it will pass on as it has hitherto done. They know not that the sceptre had slipped from the hands of the former rulers, who, within the chambers of the Three, Five and Seven, in the great tower of the Temple, now lie prone upon their faces, heroically awaiting the unrolling of the book of just judgment. The cyclone becomes a continuous storm of day after day. The rocking earth vibrates beneath their feet and trembles with each new blast of the mighty forces of Nature, wind-enveloped, drawn here by [arrogant] human will and now uncontrolled. The waters of the sea invade the land. Lashed on by the fierce currents upon their surface, the tides seem to be mounting higher and higher. It is now known that it was the sinking of the land and not the rising of the water which for ages has hidden from investigation the abodes of the richest and most powerful nation ever dwelling upon the earth. Foot by foot, all that had ever been given to us by the waters was again demanded and returned to its origin. The records of thousands of years were buried beneath the storm-tossed waters—buried but not destroyed. Only the mountain tops and the highest plateaus now known as islands remained of all the vast continent. The inland lake mingled its waters with the incoming torrent from the salty ocean, and a great gulf waters the southern shore of the country where now live in peace and wonder over the hidden past *the same reincarnated mighty race.* A few scattered books, written in stone, were saved, and a wall invisible and impermeable was built around the indestructible manuscript. Unseen and Infinite Power has thus preserved useful knowledge until the times for the revealing shall have come.

"Fear and dread for ages and ages after the awful cataclysm detained within the boundaries of their own country the feeble remnant of a people once so invincible and venturesome. The rest of the world passed on and forgot them.

"The story of the Light bearer who fell from heaven is the story of lost Atlantis. The legend of the great flood is the true narrative of facts of whose awfulness only the Atlantians had experience. They were forbidden to return to earth until the impetus of their knowledge should in some manner have spent itself, lest recurring memory tempt them to their own future pain. Thanks to the Ruler of Men, they are again to be permitted to pass out of the valley of that shadow into the possibility of new experience, life and knowledge. None but he who has lived under the awful shadow can understand what it is to exist outside of the Love currents of the universe, enveloped in the separating displeasure of the Almighty. Such is *the condition of those who seek selfish interest in preference to the good and pleasure of others.*

"Such is the story of the lost Atlantis, a world in which men had reached earthly perfection, in which all power was given to them but the power to stand face to face with God. This they could not do nor can any man. They were not satisfied with their mighty power, and, as is the case with many Masters of the present day, they try to rend the veil that separates them from the mighty presence of God—and ruin and absolute loss of power are the result. The story of Atlantis is to be a warning to all of those who would travel the Occult path. 'Thus far and no farther, mayst thou go.' It is well that all men should be careful for what purpose they use the power after they are once master of it. Once they use it for selfish purposes, all is lost."

The Future Rulers

of

America

A PHYSICIAN'S ADVENTURE

Arranged by

W. P. PHELON, M. D.

A PHYSICIAN'S ADVENTURE

I AM A PHYSICIAN. Having been in practice many years, and seen suffering in nearly all its varied forms, it would naturally happen that strange scenes of both joy and sorrow have often occurred to me. The most startling of them all, however, and the most lasting in its effect on myself commenced almost forty years ago. That was before the Civil War and very soon after being endowed with the metaphysical properties of my sheepskin. I have never outgrown the influence of that period. It has swayed all my subsequent career and will, without question, control the future lives, be they many or few.

Civil war was not then thought of as a probable thing, although perhaps deemed possible by the zealots and fire-eaters of both parties. Ominous mutterings in the political atmosphere told plainly of trouble ahead to any who could read the signs of the times. Alas! for the thousands of the blue and the gray lying side by side on a hundred battlefields, no one read or believed the writing on the scroll of the Future.

Going at once from my *Alma Mater* to a thriving town of the Southwest, I commenced practice and was from the first successful beyond my most sanguine hopes.

Three years after my location here, on New Year's Eve, a violent ringing of the night bell brought me to my feet in my bachelor quarters adjoining the office. Looking out of the open window, a darkey *silhouette* against the bright moonlight informed me:

"Massa Doctor, ole marse done sen' fer yer to cum right quick. 'Deed, but he's powerful sick."

I was young and vigorous then and rather enjoyed the excitement of night work. Kicking myself into my clothes and seizing my medicine case, the waiting darkey, who had little to say except, "Marse powerful sick," led the way from the fashionable portion of the town toward the border line between the white and colored quarters. It was a section to which my calls had been few and was unfamiliar.

At the abrupt ending of one of the fashionable avenues, the other end of which would be ashamed to confess its venture into such disreputable company, the darkey stopped before a gateway in a high, brick wall. This wall, evidently built to exclude the gaze of the curious, inclosed a whole block. My sable attendant took a key from his pocket, unlocked the wicket and, stepping inside, allowed me to precede him.

As the wicket-spring fastened itself shut, my guide rejoined me, and together we walked up the broad carriage drive toward the piazza of a large, rambling stone house. Its builders belonged to the "French Period" of the country. The shambling negro mounted the few wide stone steps leading to the piazza, letting us in by a side door, instead of the main entrance.

As the door closed behind us, a bright light flashed out from a torch in the fist of a bronze figure niched into the turn of the stairway leading to the rooms above, from the farther end of the hall.

The servant motioned me to go up. Doing as directed, in front of the top of the stairs heavy tapestry curtains over a massive door confronted me. An instant's hesitancy on my part, and the curtains, parted by invisible hands, revealed the door swinging noiselessly back. The invitation to enter was unmistakable. But a wave of something bordering on the "uncanny" swept down from head to foot as I stepped forward. I was not afraid, but—

A strangely soft, clear light filled the whole room. It seemed to emanate from nowhere in particular. Everything was as distinctly visible as if exposed to the broadest daylight. Once more that little shudder of protest against viewless power passed over me, emphasizing the consciousness of mystery realized.

The room was large and square. In one corner, on a low couch spread with rugs from Oriental looms, each representing a small fortune, lay an old man from whom life seemed fast ebbing. The unusual beauty of his youth and manhood could not be concealed by the whiteness of his long hair and beard. Even now it was not marred in a single line, but ripened into a wonderful perfection. His eyes burned with a brilliancy unbearable to the soul it pierced in its resistless intensity. The set gravity of features whose complexion was still fairer and clearer than of many a young man in his teens forbade all undue familiarity.

"Doctor," he at once began, "I have sent for you to do what might have been done by myself. But your services will be needed by me in the near future. It is desirable our acquaintance should be mutual. I have long known you and now seek simply that you may know me."

His manner while speaking was charming beyond description. There seemed to be a breaking down of all barriers between our souls, a "knitting together as one." The fascination was not unpleasant, but the invisible Ego within me recoiled uneasily at the invincibility of its power. I could make no answer and simply bowed affirmatively.

"Instead of asking a prescription from you, please do a little compounding for me. Here," taking a fine gold chain from his neck, to which was attached a silver key, "if you will open that casket, I will tell you what to do next."

His words were strange, both in their manner and in a peculiar undercurrent flowing out of them on the clear, mellow tones of his voice. This was always pitched in that far-reaching key—not high but penetrating—always assumed by the soul when partially cleaved from the cumbering body. In ordinary life mankind always recognizes this as an evidence of a cultured Soul, and they are not mistaken.

Making no delay to question, I turned at once to the casket. This rested on the heads of three golden serpents; as to their bodies, intertwined into a tripod supported on the curved ends of their tails. The casket itself, of some dark wood, blackened by its great age, looked like polished ebony. A single silver circle marked the keyhole.

The key in my hand was fashioned in the form of a human forearm and a left hand with the index finger outstretched. Mechanically I raised it to the keyhole. Did my strained nerves deceive me or did the key move by a sort of pulsation? As soft iron answers the attraction of the magnet, so this piece of silver seemed to leap forward of its own volition. Startled, the same awesome shudder I have twice mentioned crept over me. Exactly how, I knew not, but instead of the lid raising as is usual, the whole outside covering fell noiselessly away, disclosing a little chest of drawers, curiously and elaborately carved.

"Doctor," came to my ear as to one dreaming, in those musical accents, "open the upper, left-hand drawer and take out the little drinking glass and flask you will find there."

Without desire to speak, much less to question, I obeyed. The flask was about two-thirds full of what seemed to be water.

"Fill the glass half-full, and on no account remove the hand that holds the glass from contact with it." Removing the stopper from the flask, I did as directed.

"Open the right-hand lower drawer and take out the morocco case lying in the left corner. The vials within are numbered one and two. Put a single drop from each, in the order of their numbering, into the flask." As I implicitly followed his directions I seemed to receive on my left arm, which held the glass, two distinct electric shocks. Glancing up, I saw the strange light hitherto in the room had visibly waned.

Having finished the work and returned the vials carefully to their places, his next direction to me was: "Give me my potion, Doctor."

I started toward the couch. An exquisite aroma, subtle, pleasant and penetrating, seemed to emanate from the liquid and was wafted back to my nostrils. I handed him the glass. For one of those seconds rare to mortal-born—seconds that seem ages, so condensed are the sensations—all material things faded away. Even the boundaries of space vanished. There came to my soul a single flitting glimpse of the vastness of space. Upon me, awestruck, was indelibly impressed the Infinity of the Real. All this, happening while he took the glass from my hand and drained it to the bottom, was the effect upon my physical senses of this Divine fragrance.

"I shall sleep now, the sleep of Sialam.[1] It will take two days to cross the bridge that connects the Eternal Past with the Eternal Future. Come to me, Doctor, day after tomorrow morning. You will find me much more companionable then." His hand moved to a steel call-bell at the side of his couch. The sound emitted filled the whole room with a plaintive wail in a minor key. Composing himself in a relaxed attitude, he was ready for the sleep even now stealing over him.

---

[1] In a research of more than thirty-five years among Occult and mystic literature we have been able to find but two instances wherein Initiates in their writings mention the *Sleep of Sialam*. The first of these writers was the Rosicrucian Dr. Paschal Beverly Randolph in his work, *The Wonderful Story of Ravalette*, Chapter IX, Edition 1861, under the title *The Sleep of Sialam*. The second was W. P. Phelon, M.D., founder of the Hermetic Brotherhood of Atlantis, Luxor and Elphante, in the treatise now under consideration, *i.e., The Future Rulers of America*, Edition 1887. In each instance the sleep was for the purpose of looking into the future. *This is the second key.*

The servant answered the summons of the bell. Waiting at the door, he respectfully raised the tapestry as I took my departure.

"Marse allers hab sich spells New Year's Eve. Neber knew it to fail, dese twenty years, sence I lib wid him," he said, just above his breath, as he piloted me to the street.

"How long have you known him?"

"He bought me from a trader going to the sugar swamps jest twenty years ago las' Chris'mas. I was raised in ole Kaintuck."

Returning to my lodgings, my meditations on the curious actions and surroundings of my patient kept me awake until the dawn of the New Year.

Right here I must confess to a strong partiality for the hidden side of nature. I knew something of Occult law and had taken several steps in an ancient fraternity whose existence is little dreamed of by the great majority of mankind.[2] It seemed to me that some of the "missing links" in the wisdom of the ages I had so eagerly sought might come to me from this man who, having so little need of my help, appeared to be, for some purpose of his own, seeking to bind me to himself. There was no fear of him entering into my speculations upon the motive inducing him to seek my presence.

On the morning of January 2nd, having finished my round of professional visits, I found myself at the house, whose previous weird appearance was changed by the sunlight into a most charming abode, cut off from neighborly intrusion by the

---

[2] This Fraternity is as active today as it was at the time Dr. Phelon enrolled under Randolph. Its doors are open to all who sincerely seek for the *key to life*, but only a comparatively few pass beyond the first portal because the majority are actuated by purely self-interest and are unwilling to deny the *present unreality* for the future actuality. The vast number of those who appear to be in search of the Grail are not students with sincere aims, but mere dabblers in the science of the Soul.

high brick walls and imperious gates.

The wicket opened readily at the ringing of the bell. Passing on up to the main entrance, the heavy mahogany doors stood wide open, disclosing the great hall with its perfectly polished floor. The furnishing was scanty, but all in the most exquisite taste and elegant workmanship.

The servitor appeared on the stairs as I crossed the threshold.

"Marse done ben 'spectin' yer." He led me once more into the presence of my illustrious patient. He was seated in a low easy chair, smoking an Oriental chibouk. He acknowledged my presence by a nod. All trace of weariness or distress had left him; he had evidently taken a new lease of life on much more favorable terms.

"You see, I am better, Doctor. You are in good time. Have but just finished my bath and breakfast. Be seated." He indicated a chair at his right hand. I sat and chatted a few moments. This was the beginning of an acquaintance, to me, of sincere pleasure, bringing as it did a priceless acquisition of arcane wisdom.

Our acquaintance lasted a year. All my leisure hours were spent in his company. Our range of discussion embraced the most abstruse subjects, on all of which he had knowledge and well-defined ideas, speaking as "one having authority and not as the scribes."

On one of the late fall days, as we sat on the broad piazza, he read to me, as from an invisible book, the terrible events of the coming, now past, years; of rivers of blood, and of the advent of peace; then of still more fearful disaster to our common country which is yet to come; finally, of a small but chastened remnant who would see with their eyes and hear with their ears and be healed of all infirmities of body and mind, a fit seed for a new and mighty nation. It is coming nearer,

nearer![3] God help us all!

During all this time he had revealed to me but little of his personality. While I knew of him, I did not know him any more than many who were strangers to me. Aside from his charming eloquence and incomparable wisdom, he was an unsolved equation. However, the sad occasion when I should know more of him was all too rapidly approaching.

It was a year to a day from that memorable night when I first saw him that the darkey summoned me at early evening, saying as soon as he saw me:

"Marse got 'nudder spell. Cum right quick. Nebber see him so strange."

As on the former occasion, so now, I found him reclining on his couch, waiting my coming.

"Doctor," he began, his melodious voice thrilling me with an affectionate cadence he had never before so openly displayed, "the hour is coming when choice will be given me to

---

[3] The present period of stress and strife. A conflict of Communism, Naziism, Bolshevism, Fascism, Communistic Laborism and Nihilism, movements in most part led by Soulless leaders who, consciously or unconsciously, are doing their best to destroy both the rights of labor and property without the least benefit to any but the few egomaniacs who, like the Piper, lead the workers into a vast ocean of delusion from which there is no exit. It is a destructive Collectivism against Individualism, and the rights of the laborer, both mental and physical, to enjoy the fruits of his efforts, are being destroyed. It is the destruction of the weak and innocent, as in Ethiopia and China; the great nations of the world too weak, vacillating or inert to outlaw the perpetrators of the heinous crimes and thereby bringing the reaction of the Law upon themselves, just as surely as though they themselves were guilty of these crimes. It is the age of the scrapping of solemnly signed treaties, rights of the weak or lesser peoples, rights of neutrals, of civilized warfare and property without a serious protest by those who were signatories. Truly, it is a time of "those whom the Gods would destroy," and those who will be destroyed, or more correctly, *who are destroying themselves*, are NOT alone these inhuman aggressors, but the strong who permit it without demanding an accounting. There is but *one* remedy; *not* war, but the firm outlawing of those who respect neither treaties nor rights of others by all nations and peoples not engaged in the inhuman destruction.

lay aside the habiliments of earthly existence or to endure the monotonies of another cycle. I choose now to lay away this mortal in which I have so long lingered, seizing once more upon untrammeled immortality, the birthright of all men. To you, Doctor, I am about to commit the knowledge of my personality in the past, hitherto known only to myself. On the desk you will find necessary materials. Your ability as a stenographer will compass the rest."

Overborne by the weight of approaching calamity, I obeyed implicitly his directions. That which follows is a verbatim report of the disclosure, taken down as it fell from the lips of this wonderful man. It has been long kept sacredly, but the time is now ripe, and it is made public for the first time:

"Of Phœnician birth, I was an old man, as mortals reckon, when Hiram, King of Tyre, held the throne of that proud nation. My education in the temple had made me a member of the priesthood. Periodical allotment finally sent me to a colony originally planted on the Pacific coast of Central America.

"For many years we prospered as a trading colony. As a part of the national priesthood, we had advisory charge of all matters of interest to our people. My desire to perceive the Truth had been rewarded, and I was respected for my learning, as well as for the position that was mine in the Temple.

"After the conquest of Tyre by Alexander and the loss of prestige thereby, the home government left the colonies to shift for themselves. We were much troubled by the continued invasions of the warlike tribes from the North. Our city was so situated that impregnable defense was impossible. Finally, directed by 'Those Who Know,' we emigrated eastward in a body into the mountain belt, where we were assured of protection and rest. Scouts were sent out, who brought back news of a delightful country whose entrance could easily be defended against our outside foes.

"The way was long and, under the most favorable conditions, exceedingly difficult for the tender feet of our women and children. Many of the weaker members of our community perished on this journey.

"We were led directly up to apparently impassable snow-crowned peaks. At the last moment, when we had even begun to doubt the fealty of our guides, we perceived a narrow canyon, the cleft resembling in the distance a hair on the snowy surface. Growing as we approached it, we found it ample for both ourselves and the accompanying train. A few miles of sheltered travel brought us to a scene never surpassed upon this planet.

"If the Aidenn-land of our traditions had been securely kept for us, it could not have been more beautiful than the hidden plateau now unrolled before our snow-dazzled eyes and weary feet. A vast plain stretched away hundreds of square miles, all covered with a semi-tropical vegetation. In the center a lake of unfailing supply, whose fathomless depths yielded no secret to the curious eye, suggested the inland sea that probably preceded it. From this, on every side, rolling plains spread as far as the eye could reach to the base of the inclosing mountains. Here abrupt precipices arose perpendicularly into mid-air. A plummet dropped at the apex would swing clear at the base. It appeared as if, by some mighty volcanic wrench or subsidence, the whole plateau had been smoothly split from its attachments, sunk and then been raised until the waters drained off through the central lake.[4]

---

[4] Reader, did you by any chance see the scenario *The Lost Horizon,* or, perchance, read the book of that title? Is it possible that you still remember the description of that inland Paradise? If so, then compare what you read or saw with the description here given in this treatise issued in 1887, a booklet largely circulated more than fifty years ago by one of the August Fraternity. It is the ideal of a Master made real by means of the scenario and a prophecy of what *is to be* when men actually accept the doctrine of the New Age (the beginning of which is

"Beside the clear waters our tired people slept. In the morning a single earthquake shock awakened us. This must have been the last of a series. Nothing of the kind has since disturbed us during the following centuries. It might have been the controlling direction of a powerful human will. I cannot explain. Nothing special was thought of it until an attempt was made to reach the outer world. We then found that the canyon through which we had entered had ceased to exist. We were hopelessly prisoners, for no means within our reach, if we desired it, could give us, without long years of arduous training, exit over or through those mighty walls of rock, ever sentineled by the snow-helmeted crags of ice.

"At least we were secure from our foes; naught but winged creatures could come to us or go hence by ordinary means.

"Resigning ourselves to our fate, we set to work at once to utilize all our resources and whatever our new country contained. To this end, we brought to bear the light of all the wisdom already acquired and sought incessantly to draw from the great source of all knowledge new supplies.

"Under laws devised to meet the conditions of this new world, of which we were sole occupants, we built a city and a temple. The temple was hewed directly into the face of the mightiest cliff. The façade and carvings of the entrance were equaled only by those of the great Temple of Luxor, of which, you must understand, our priesthood was a direct branch.

"Every year has added to the excavations made in the heart of the mountain, and the metallic treasures yielded up have supplied abundantly our necessities. Inch by inch, we have been nearing the outer air. When that is reached the jubilee will be proclaimed.

"The nation has constantly aimed to perfect its solidarity.

---

now), of Personal Responsibility, and *live accordingly*. **Here is the Third Key.**

All its arts and sciences are peace-compelling. The population has increased in numbers, but not so rapidly as it would have done on a lower physical plane.

"The priests, of whom many came in through the mountain cleft, have neither forgotten nor lost sight of the tumultuous world outside. Their communication with it is perfect. They can see, however, no benefit that could accrue to their people from the unrestful selfishness with which you are so familiar.

"The people have forgotten their ingress, save as a faint tradition. Coming events inspire them, and they are looking forward to the day of their enlargement. While patiently waiting, they are constantly growing into that wisdom which makes the spirit dominant over all things, created and uncreated.

"Horses came in with the original caravan, but no other animal. The people eat no flesh, sustaining life upon sun-cooked food, fruits and grains. Seeds of various plants, both textile and eatable, were brought in by us, and the best and most delicious fruits were already growing in our Garden of Eden when we took possession.

"The temperature varies but little during the solar cycle. The absence of gross stimulation to the nerve tension induced by meat eating and the evenness of the temperature prevents the fret and worry so wasteful of the energies of your people.

"Could any people be developed under more favorable circumstances for the handling of unseen powers and forces, of which mankind at large neither dreams nor cares? It is the true perception of the Infinite guided by Wisdom and inspired by Goodness. They think and move as one in alignment with Creative Energy and can prevail against all the nations of the earth. As it was written in the elder day: 'five can chase a hundred, and a hundred shall put ten thousand to flight, and their enemies shall fall before them by the sword.'

"It will not be possible for any nation, no matter how

skilled in the arts and weapons of physical destruction, to stand before them. All must yield or be destroyed. Thus far these powers have been used simply to make beautiful and habitable their City of Promise.

"There is a prophecy in the astral currents, declaring: Within a hundred years this marvelous people, so quietly waiting the hour of their freedom, unaffected by the mischievous follies and vicious beliefs of men, will be set free from their probationary prison and come forth to rule the earth. It will be the second coming of the Truth."[5]

Here my patient paused for breath. His feelings, ordinarily self-controlled, had risen to ecstasy, as his prophetic vision saw the coming triumph of his people. It would be a full realization to them of faithful trust in the possibilities of a far-off future.

He lay a few moments quietly, then, rousing himself, resumed:

"I have hoped to welcome them here, for I am forbidden by mine oath to bring back to them this load of clay. It matters nothing, however, for once free of the mortal, I can again mingle with them even more freely than ever before.

"You wonder how and why I am here, and they there. It is the old story. Simply because curiosity and desire for ex-

---

[5] Fifty years have passed since this prophecy was made. We are now exactly in the middle period of the hundred years. The leaven is working, the mass is agitated; shortly the clarification and elimination of destructive forces and their henchmen will begin, and nations condoning satanic agitators and trouble-brewers, women-rapers and child destroyers will be cast into the limbo of forgotten things. The despoilers of Ethiopia will be simmering in their own brew; the rapers of China will be an exploited people; Collectivism, like the doctrine of free silver, will have given way to Individualism; the laborer paid the wages of his efforts; the shirker receiving his just dues, and the strong helping the weak to *help themselves* and become strong, *not* by having their burdens lifted from their shoulders, but by helping them gain the strength to carry on so that they, like all others, will perform their part in the drama of life.

perience led me to request leave of my superior, the high priest, to banish myself from their company, so long as I cared to wear the 'coats of skin.'

"Assisted by my comrades in the exercise of powers known to me, I transferred myself bodily beyond the mountains. It was a sad parting, as I bound myself by oath never to return until I had given the dust to the dust from which it came.

"I have fully measured the littleness of the knowledge of those who claim to be the wisest of men. I know how strangely your scientists are deceived in their study for the Real. I can see how phantom-like are all their gleanings, for they see only the shadow and not the substance. There is nothing in the whole wide world for whose attainment I would linger one single instant. I long for my spirit's freedom, which shall bring me to my friends once more. They have been able in all these years to come to me. I know from them all that has taken place there. In fifteen minutes my centuries-long earth-life will end, and I shall be FREE."

I followed his eye to the clock, an antique. The dial formed the circle above the cross, inclosed within the interlacing triangles of the Rosecrucian[6] symbol. It was one-quarter of twelve.

"To you, my dear Doctor, in whom is the pure gold of the alchemist, legal transference from me will give possession of all that now surrounds you. I give you this key" (handing me the little silver key, which had not been seen by me since last New Year's Eve). "I need not say, put the contents of the casket to a good use, for I know you will. There are men liv-

[6] Recall to mind that this story was printed and circulated in the year 1887—fifty years ago—that it was written by a member of the August Fraternity or Brotherhood still laboring for the welfare of humanity. Bear in mind that with a special purpose in view and as a *key* the author spelled the word "Rosecrucian" instead of Rosicrucian, thereby conserving for the Fraternity the choice of either spelling. *This is the Fourth Key.*

ing who would give untold millions to know even one of its many secrets."

He then took from his neck a flexible band of steel. Upon this swung a small, flat, metallic case. Putting it into my hands, he said: "A year from tonight, in some place alone, where your quiet and privacy will not be disturbed, look upon this mirror, and you shall have news from me and mine that may do you good.

"But my friends are coming to accompany me to the Beautiful City of Peace."

A chill, as of a gust from a suddenly opened outer door, passed over me. I looked up. In two chairs by the couch sat forms of ashen gray, perfectly outlined and visible. Their figures were of ancient men, revered and wise.

My patient said: "Doctor, these are my friends, still in the flesh, who have come to greet the real me when my release shall be accomplished. Say ye not so, my comrades?" In answer, like the sonorous chimes of a far-off cathedral bell, came their words, floating out of the silence: "Yea, we are here, as thou hast requested, to tell you we desire and wait for your return, giving you both greeting and welcome. As we speak, so say all of our people."

"Farewell, Doctor." As my patient spoke, I saw that the supreme moment mortals call dissolution was upon him. Death was claiming its inheritance. The eyes closed; a sighing gasp succeeded.

The two visitors, rising, stood expectantly, their garments flowing to their sandaled feet. They wait one, two minutes. I see distinctly in the clear light a third figure formulated. It stands with them. Its presence seems a matter of congratulation to them all. A slight noise at the door, caused by the old colored servant's entrance, diverts my gaze for a single instant.

I look back. I am alone.

I hold in my hands the key to his casket, the mirror and the manuscript.

The household are aroused. The usual preliminaries, and the Master's body is entombed with all due ceremony, respect and propriety.

His lawyers informed me that, after providing liberally for his three servants, I was left the house and grounds and the remainder of his possessions, on the single condition of living there one year.

What happened during that year or at the end of it is no part of this story. Sufficient to say I am an old man, and it is the most wonderful experience of a long life.

The
BROTHERHOOD *of*
THE ROSY CROSS

❧

The First World Parliament
and
MEETING OF THE
COUNCIL OF SEVEN

❧

THE CONSECRATION
OF WASHINGTON
The Deliverer

❧

FULFILMENT OF
THE PROPHECY

Published by
THE ROSICRUCIAN FOUNDATION
(REGISTERED)
BEVERLY HALL · QUAKERTOWN, PA.

BIOGRAPHY

GEORGE LIPPARD, Philosophic Initiate, genius, dreamer, champion of the oppressed; advocate of the freedom of man; visionary, yet practical reformer; awakener of Lincoln to the negro's plight; founder of a Brotherhood of Man and author of many books, was born on April 10, 1822.

After graduating from the public school, he entered the Classical Academy, at Rhinebeck, New York, and later was enrolled in the Wesleyan University, a religious institution, at Middletown, Connecticut.

Lippard's ideas of right and wrong developed at an extremely early age. Because of his early mental-spiritual development, he quickly and keenly recognized the wide gap existing between the ideals and teachings in a religious institution such as the Wesleyan University.

Try as he would, it was impossible for him to reconcile himself to the difference between professions and pretensions, his sense of right being such that it was impossible for him to be hypocritical. Lippard was unable to recognize any middle ground. An act would be either right or wrong and there could be no excuse, no extenuating circumstances for on professing right to commit a wrong.

It is almost unbelievable, but of record, that young Lippard at the age of a little more than fifteen became a student in the law office of William Badger and then later entered the office of Ovid Fraser Johnaon, who subsequently became Attorney-General of the State of Pennsylvania.

However, after a period of four years in the law offices, he acquired the same conception of Law and lawyers as he had previously of the church and ministry. Now, at the age of twenty years and wiser in the ways of life than most men were at the age of eighty, he entered the field of journalism by accepting employment on the Philadelphia daily, *Spirit of the Times*.

Lippard's spiritual training began shortly after he started in journalism and became an author and lecturer on what he termed the "Legends" of the American Revolution. At this time he came into touch with the then active COUNCIL OF THREE of The Rosy Cross and was impressed with their sincerity and warmth for the welfare of the downtrodden.

As with all else, he took up the WORK with heart and Soul and soon was one of the most devoted Acolytes of the FRATERNITAS, sufficiently advanced to be permitted to take an active part in the COUNCIL. At the age of twenty-one, even though not yet a member of the Council he had attained to Philosophic Initiation. (There is record of only one other instance of an American Acolyte's having atttained at the age of twenty-one.)

By the time he was twenty-five he had accomplished the Great Work; had become a member of the Brethren of Light; was made a member of the Council.

To Major General Ethan Allan Hitchcock must be given the credit for being the spiritual Father in later years of Lippard, Lincoln, and Randolph, their sponsor and guide in their search for Philosophic Initiation.

It was General Hitchcock who introduced Lippard to Lincoln and then to Randolph. It was Lippard who aroused Lincoln's interest in the freedom of the negro. It was Lippard who finally convinced Lincoln that, should opportunity offer, the slaves should be given their freedom. It was the Legends written by Lippard, first widely circulated separately, and then in a volume known as *The White Banner*, that caused Lincoln to make his final decision.

A partial list of his writings reveals around thirty superb works. He brought about mighty reforms in the realms of law, religion, man's dealings with man, and the elimination of negro slavery.

Lippard was a truly great Rose Cross, and, at the youthful age of 32, on February 9, 1854, passed into the Great Beyond, the realm of Light, beloved by all who knew him.

See BOOK OF ROSICRUCIAE this publisher for further details.

INTRODUCTION

One hundred and thirteen years ago there was born in the City of Philadelphia, one who in a brief life-span of only thirty-two years was to accomplish more for the Brotherhood of the Rosy Cross than any other single person, and, yet, who was to become almost unknown a few years after his passing.

George Lippard was born during the period when the very air in the eastern section of Pennsylvania was vibrant with the spirit of freedom. Men thought, talked and dreamed freedom—freedom of speech, freedom of action, freedom of rights.

It seemed that all men whose nature inclined them to Freedom were drawn together by a mystic link and that they were impelled by one motive and one object—to cast aside the last shackles by which they were bound to the moloch of creed and caste which was degrading all but the few. They sensed the sham of an artificial democracy which had followed the over-throw of a king's rule, for while the government existed in the name of "Democracy" it was actually in the hands and under the influence of a coterie of men who still retained all of the old world pride of birth and aristocracy of viewpoint.

Early in life Lippard came into close contact with several members of the Council of the Rosy Cross. He was by nature and inclination perfectly fitted to absorb the Mystic Lore of those men who had labored so many hundreds of years for the freedom of man and he delved with eagerness into the tomes of the histories of man and of the Mystic movement. Through oral transmission he was trained in the principles and purposes of the August Fraternity and in an outline of the mission before him. He was informed fully of the sufferings borne by the sectarians before they came to American shores in 1694; of the preparation and fight for the liberty of the new world which began in 1773 and culminated in 1777; of the movement to free man from old world rule and influence that a republican form of government might be established in the interest of all men; and of that work soon to be begun of striking the shackles of human slavery from the black race.

Lippard was a Mystic and a dreamer by nature, but he was more than a dreamer, for he was fearless and he was prepared always

1

to fight for a principle he felt to be right. From the moment of his contact with the members of the Brotherhood, he was converted to every thought and every plan outlined by them and he immediately enrolled with the Council that he might enter upon his training in preparation for what he was to do. When his preparation was accomplished he came completely under the conviction that it was his particular mission to awaken men to a full understanding of the true meaning of freedom and to bring them to the recognition that in its true sense it was yet to be realized. To this end he embodied his thought in the form of writings that were facts clothed with fiction. His first volume appeared when he was but twenty-two years of age and success as an author followed almost immediately, although he was bitterly assailed by that "better class" of society which was guilty of the very injustices which he sought with all the power of his pen to attack and expose.

When he was but twenty-six he had so far proceeded with his Initiation into the Brotherhood that he requested permission to incorporate the history of the Brotherhood and of the Council in the form of a novel. This was readily granted and his purpose found its achievement in several novels. The two most important were THE LEGENDS OF THE AMERICAN REVOLUTION OF 1776 and PAUL ARDENHEIM, THE MONK OF WISSAHICKON, in which were disclosed many facts concerning the activities of the Brotherhood.

Before the age of thirty Lippard became one of the most successful authors of his day. He had edited a newspaper which had quickly accomplished a circularization of fifty thousand; he had seen the crowds fill to overflowing the theatre in which one of his books was produced as a play and yet, notwithstanding, he was wholly dissatisfied with his actual accomplishments in the interest of freedom.

During the period he was under training with the Brotherhood and while he was preparing those novels in which he relates some of the history of the Brotherhood's activities, it was his dream and hope that those men who sought improvement in conditions would be drawn to the Brotherhood and that they would readily undergo the arduous training through which they might secure for themselves true freedom. In this dream he met with disappointment, for he soon learned that while all are willing to accept the fruits of freedom, comparatively few are willing to undergo the work and sacrifice necessary for its achievement. This realization came as a great shock to him, but it brought to his mind the thought that his purpose could be accomplished to some degree at least by the

2

establishment of an order which would inculcate in its members the teachings of the Great Master and the principles of true freedom.

In fulfillment of his idea he created that order which is now known as the Brotherhood of America. The members of this secret patriotic organization were instructed in the true principles of Brotherhood, but were not required to subscribe to the training of self-denial and personal effort necessary to become actually members of the Brotherhood of the Rosy Cross.

Lippard was not robust, and possessed as he was, of an intense nature, the demands of his spirit proved too great for the strength of his physical body. His unwillingness to permit himself the necessary rest and recuperation after strenuous efforts, was responsible for his death on February 9, 1854, at the age of thirty-two. In a short space of thirty-two years he had accomplished more than a vast majority of men achieve in a century. He immortalized his name, and although as yet it does not appear upon the pages of history, the time is not very distant when it will receive the recognition it so well deserves.

Lippard was actively associated in the last few years of his life with his contemporary in the fight for freedom, Dr. P. B. Randolph, and both men were aggressive members of the movement which was then known as the Reformatory party. They were both radical in a sense. Randolph was fiery of nature, one of the best orators of his time, capable of completely imbuing his audience with his theme and of holding hundreds spellbound for hours at a time. It was as a speaker that Lincoln so often drafted him with unusual success. Lippard the dreamer, the Mystic, fiery of nature too, was a propagandist, a master in his own way at commanding and retaining the attention of the public. Each was a master—both served well.

The first part of this Monograph the PARLIAMENT OF THE WORLD, THE BROTHERHOOD OF THE ROSY CROSS is verbatim from the book PAUL ARDENHEIM, THE MONK OF THE WISSAHICKON, while the CONSECRATION OF THE DELIVERER GEORGE WASHINGTON is verbatim from the LEGENDS OF THE AMERICAN REVOLUTION 1776, both by George Lippard.

Research and references to written and verbal history of the activities of the Brotherhood show both legends to be based on fact and they may be accepted as such except in some minor and unimportant detail. No changes have been made in the text. Comment and annotation are in foot-note form, but since it was undesirable to add explanations more copious than the foot-notes would permit, references have also been included in the preamble. Symbols in the text refer to specific comment in the preamble which has been compiled with a continuity which permits reading, if the reader prefers, without relation to the text itself. This is a departure from the usual method of annotation and we trust the reader will be pleased with it.

R. SWINBURNE CLYMER.

Beverly Hall.
February 12, 1935.

PREAMBLE

It is passing strange that the truly great figures of history, those who have been known as the leaders of their time in all periods and in all countries, have not been churchmen nor have they been active members of organized formal lodges. This was particularly true of the early leaders of thought and action in America. Few indeed of those who assisted in creating the New Republic and who wrote and signed the Declaration of Independence and the Constitution, were churchmen. Many of them were known as atheists and agnostics. But while such men may not have been churchmen in the usual sense of the term, there have been but few of the really great that have not been actually religious in thought and in spirit. It has been the memory and recognition of the conflicts and persecutions of organized religion that has driven the true leader from the formal church and lodge. Yet with few exceptions the motivations of those who have risen to acknowledged leadership have been a love of humanity and a recognition of principles of true religion which they sought to bring to a more vivid realization.

[1] Through all the ages, amongst all the true leaders who have had the welfare of their peoples at heart, there is the evidence that the driving force animating their purpose has been those principles which appear identical with the precepts which the church, regardless of denomination, purports to hold and to inculcate. Churchmen these great leaders of the past may not have been, but regardless of what they may have been called, not one who has left a deep mark in history has been actually an agnostic or an atheist. Almost without exception, each has been in the true sense devoutly religious. This thought is expressed by one who was active in the beginning of the present New Dispensation which began in 1884. He wrote, "We do not have to depend upon churches and lodges for initiation into the grandest mysteries of God; for the heavens are open—and in the spaces above are countless multitudes that with thought and act are baptizing the earth with all you are capable of receiving. Then arise in your thought [and desire] and meet them." * Despite the apparent agnosticism of the writer he was a truly religious man, deeply mystic and sublimely philosophical,

---

* *Temple of the Rosy Cross*—Freeman B. Dowd—Edition 1901, page 321.

ever ready to meet with others in conclaves and convocations if they were for the betterment of the people and inspired by the purpose of advancing the Brotherhood of Man. To this end he took an active part in the Second World Parliament.

[2] The First World Parliament convened during a period when the new world was inhabited by men of many lands, and had not yet achieved entity or independence. If the legends of this First World Parliament are but half-truths—and legends often merely clothe actual fact—then America owes its independence and its freedom to the members of that Council of Universal Brotherhood who gathered together in the long ago for secrecy and counsel in an old world cavern.

[3] History is not necessarily fact regardless of by whom the fact may have been related. It can be but little more than a fabric composed partly of truth and partly of prejudice that virtually is falsehood. Man is biased by prejudice and passion. He sees what he chooses to see and he colors this to produce what he wants to see. Under stress of war he can see neither courage nor justice nor virtue in the enemy or his cause and he deems it high treason even to express sympathy with or recognition of the opposing point of view. Most of all history is based upon a bias that frustrates the truth and reflects the opinion of observers who are blinded either by personal feeling, or the sentiment of the time or the fear of the consquence of non-conformity. At best it deals with effects rather than with causes. It relates much of no real importance and knows little of either the forces or the personal actions which produced the effects with which it deals. Many of the great events of history were but the surface reflections of trends created by the tireless efforts and sacrifices of those who are unknown or obscure in related history.

[4] *All* reformations have been at best but a fleeting benefit to the world generally for human nature continues much the same and the reformers of today become the tyrants of tomorrow, irrespective of name or creed or country. Whatever the relief measures they produce are only a passing benefit and they usually benefit some at the expense of others. The Parliaments held by the secret brotherhoods whether in the past ages or in the present age have all had to do with the betterment of man. The Fraternity of the Rosy Cross—Fraternitas Rosae Crucis—has as its express aim and purpose the benefit of humanity. In a sense it desires reformation, but it believes that there is only one *true reformation,* and that that deals with man—the individual. True reform is not accom-

6

plished by social or political revolutions nor by the destruction of one group by another, but by the evolution, the re-formation of the man himself through the acceptance of the true Law which governs human relationship. To benefit one at the cost of another does not enrich him whom we seek to benefit, for no real benefit may come to him that he has not earned. Consequently his gain at the loss of another would inevitably reflect to his ultimate loss since the Law of Compensation will again take from him that which is not truly his. Man—the individual—must reform himself. He must learn and apply the Law of Personal Responsibility. He must come to the understanding of that Law under which alone true democracy can function and he must recognize and apply it in its two aspects, that of brotherhood and that of compensation. His dealings must be on the basis of fair exchange; he may neither take nor accept that which he has not earned unless he exchanges for it something of equal value. He must know that whatever he takes to himself that he has not earned the Law itself will again take from him in some manner or other; that whatever he receives even as a gift but which he has not earned will likewise be taken from him. This is a true doctrine through which man can accomplish his evolution. Its application begins with the acceptance of the Law which is the Law of *True Manhood,* or Personal Responsibility. This is a true reformation of man. It is a government of himself against the urge of his baser animal nature and until reformation is accomplished by the individual re-forming or transforming himself, all other attempts at reformation by civil, social or religious means ultimately will fail.

⁵ Man cannot be reformed by instant conversion; by code, creed, preaching nor by priests, kings or dictators; nor by legislative enactment or penal laws; nor can man be saved by coercion, no matter how well-intentioned the force may be or by whom it is directed. Man can accomplish reformation only through himself and he can assist in the accomplishment of the reformation of others only by knowing this Law, applying it and teaching it to others. Whenever man learns to comprehend the one Universal Law, when he becomes conscious of the fact that it actually pays to obey that Law, then will there be a true reformation, without force and without bloodshed. Then governments, churches, all of the institutions of mankind will inevitably reflect the reformation that man has achieved for himself, through his own efforts.

⁶ Union, Freedom and Brotherhood, great and desirable ideals, are seemingly the heritage of all. But of what benefit are they to

7

the man or the nation who has not yet learned the Law? What power or benefit is there in a union unless that union cements with the common acknowledgment of Universal Law those whom it strives to hold together? Freedom—of what value is freedom to those who seek to use it only as license without regard to the rights of others? No man can be free although the whole earth be laid at his feet unless he understands the Law and is willing as an individual to apply it. And when he understands the Law and applies it, he is free even though bound by the shackles of society, government and church. Only when man recognizes that he is free, when he knows and obeys the Law, will he be fit for freedom. If he receives it before he is fit for it, he will simply turn but from one master to another. Brotherhood defeats its very declaration when it seeks to coerce. It exists only as an emanation of love from the heart of that man who does not seek to take from others a freedom which he desires to possess for himself.

[7] Freedom, Unity, Brotherhood can be no more than ideals until men learn first within themselves their meaning and as individuals, in their own lives, apply the knowledge. Then will they have freedom. Then will they not seek power and special privilege and advantage for themselves that they may control and exploit others. Brotherhood does not give the strong the right to dictate to others what they shall do. Freedom is not that license which encroaches on the right of another. Freedom and Brotherhood are rights and privileges which man may only gain and use without injury to himself when he accepts the Law of Personal Responsibility. Freedom, Unity and Brotherhood is the religion of the truly strong. It is the Law of Manhood. It is the vision of John the Revelator and its values may only be secured as man individually evolves to claim them.

[8] There is neither evil nor good, neither salvation nor destruction in a title. A tyrant may be good; the president of a republic, evil. Regardless of who may wield it, a power unwisely used results in destruction and misery. Reformation usually starts as a rebellion against tyranny and ends in a form of tyranny as great as it overthrew. The tyrant sought to retain his power that he might exploit his fellowmen. The reform leader, taking advantage of the reaction against tyranny, secures power and promptly turns it to the same end as did the tyrant while man supports first the one and then the other because he will not learn to govern himself. His only weapon for his self-protection and the defense of his own rights is in seeking to apply first in his own life the principles which

8

he endeavors to have expressed by his government and its representatives. Freedom is an ideal only so long as man refuses to apply its principles in his relationship to others. It becomes an actuality in the experience of the individual to the extent that it is applied by him. *Man must learn to govern himself.*

[9] Freedom cannot be retained after it has been secured unless men in truth as individuals have *become* free men. The masses of any country on the globe today may be delivered from the hands of a king or an emperor or a protector or a dictator, and yet tomorrow place themselves in bondage again to some other form of tyranny. For unless man understands what truly constitutes freedom he cannot know what to do with it when he has gained it and he becomes the victim of the ambitious, the crafty and the cruel who secure their power only through preying on the ignorance and the fear of the weak. As man, the individual, frees himself from his own ignoble passions, emotions, desires, fears, weaknesses, he develops the strength which protects him from exploitation, abuse or control at the hands of another. He may begin to secure his freedom only as he begins to comprehend and accept the Law of Personal Responsibility: *that man may not benefit at the expense of a fellow creature without ultimately paying for the benefit seemingly derived in equal coin with usurious interest.* History teaches us this in fiery letters but we are blind to the facts with which we are confronted on every side and at every angle.

[10] The masses struggling for freedom have turned from king to priest, from priest to tyrant and back to king and have found no relief from suffering, bloodshed, cruelty, all forms of abuse and exploitation at the hands of each in turn. Time and time again throughout history man, with the gift of freedom in his hands, has relinquished it to those mad with a lust for power. It was left to the twentieth century to prove that power in the hands of a commoner may be abused to as great an extent as it is in the hands of royalty. Dictators who have risen from the humble of the earth and become drunk with power have inflicted tyrannies and enslaved the masses as did the kings and priests of old. Justice is not born in all men, and without justice slavery is inevitable. In the new age if man's dream of freedom is to be materialized, justice must be enthroned in the heart of every man and each must come to a recognition of its Law. He will know then that the *Law itself punishes* and that the injustice for which he individually is responsible is but reflected in the injustice which he must suffer with the *reaction* of the Law, at the hands of another. King, dictator,

9

tyrant, priest, each wins his power and retains it because man will not be just to man. In the new age as man learns and begins to apply the law of love, as he *becomes* in the true sense a Free Man, seeking justice for all rather than favor to himself, then will his priests and kings reflect justice, and slavery will disappear from the face of the earth.

[11] In the old dispensation as soon as those men who had suffered at the hands of tyrants freed themselves and secured power, they set themselves up as judges and executioners even as the tyrant from whom they had stripped all power. The old Law from which has come suffering, cruelty and enslavement has been "do as we do, believe as we believe—or be damned." To refuse obedience to the dictates of the rulers under this law is high treason. In its name the vilest and the most terrible atrocities have been committed upon those who refuse to bend the knee, in the name either of country or of God. Those under whose dictates this old law has been enforced through the guillotine, the inquisition and the scaffold are not alone responsible. The masses who have accepted and applied this false intolerance in their own relationships with others have been responsible, for the people themselves have actually formulated the law which their leaders have but reflected. All men who understand the Law of the New Dispensation will govern themselves to the end of reflecting justice and tolerance and love for their fellowmen. They will know, since they understand the True Law, that as they abuse or defraud another, so in turn will the Law provide the punishment by which they will be abused and defrauded by another.

[11a] The esoteric section of the August Fraternity is universal and it oversees all the work of the Grand Fraternity—the Fraternitas Rosae Crucis. In this Brotherhood those of certain rank and station may know those who are below them but they may not know who are above them in station. Those of the Brotherhood are rarely known either to their brethren or the world at large as Rosicrucians. They are engaged in worthy avenues of activity as physicians, lawyers, musicians, statesmen and artisans. They do not seek to be known of men. They are satisfied but to adhere to the Law and fulfill their destiny on earth. They are swayed neither by friendship, flattery, hatred nor fear. Such "Rosicrucians think very little of the ways of the world—its pride, arrogance and dignity—they are simple for they find the truth to be simple. The fruits of truth are free from pretense. These men *are* initiates and *free* in all essentials,—free to think, to be and to express themselves—always for the good of others and in the cause of prog-

10

ress." * They cannot be intimidated nor can they be persecuted. They do not issue written credentials or documents of authority to anyone although they may delegate powers to others for given purposes. They cannot be exposed because their brethren, with the exception of those above them, do not know them. They cannot bring shame upon the fraternity because of some unworthy act or acts that the world might consider unworthy because their acts are merely acts of the individual. "Only by their fruits may ye know them." These men of the esoteric section of the *Rosicruciae* work in secret because of their knowledge of the Law that the potent forces of nature are silent, secret and unknown. They manifest themselves openly at times but only in some unselfish and worthy cause. Their true work is spiritual—the welfare and guidance of mankind. They have nothing in common with materialism except intellectually. Since they have no affinity with materialism they have no materialistic golden plan to lure men into *a semblance* of brotherly love and fellowship. Unobtrusive, unpretending they pass through life looking with eyes of pity upon a world of gold and treasure and material power as upon children building sand castles that the sea must wash away. They are seldom understood and for this reason, their silence. They are in the world but they are not of it. Their wish is to do their work quietly but without evasion of any aspect of it. Since they know they may leave the world and its experiences only through accomplishing their own evolution by doing good, they secretly do all within their power to help their fellowmen. They are conscious of having been sent here for that purpose—to help the world in its efforts to immortalize the race—and to establish True Brotherhood. These men are interested in forming no political party nor do they use their adherents for the purpose of swaying the judgment of anyone in power except for *race* benefit but their power is great, nevertheless, for when their fiat is cast it is absolute since they know the Law, work with it and the Law itself accomplishes that which is in harmony with it. They know that governments and society are neither better nor worse than those who support them. They are not "radical" in their desire for change nor are they reformers in the generally accepted sense for they know that a new order may only come as men free themselves from their own individual weaknesses and evils. They are painfully aware that before True Brotherhood may be established, man himself must undergo that evolution which

---

* *Temple of the Rosy Cross*—F. B. Dowd, 1901 Edition, pages 312-13.

can come only from an individual recognition of the Law and obedience in observing it. They know that not until then will man be truly free.

[12] The Rosicrucians are of all nationalities and of all climes. They meet occasionally, drawn together not by press notices or the ringing of bells but by a common need of the spirit. The men of *Rosicrucae* form a Fraternity in its true sense * rather than an Order, although in some instances Orders veiled in profound secrecy have materialized successfully. Men fear what they do not know and consequently it is dangerous to possess a knowledge beyond that of the masses. The proverbial secrecy of the Brothers of the Rosy Cross is necessary if for no other reason than that now, as always, the Brotherhood has engaged in the most profound study, investigation and experimentation in its endeavor to aid the advancement of the race. And now as in the past in many countries of the world it would be hardly safer for members to be known than in the seventeenth century when the First World Council convened in a cavern in Germany. The brethren of the esoteric section of the Fraternity whose members are more numerous today than ever before, shroud themselves in a cloud of mystery.** They know that all power is a mystery and they but follow the admonition of their Great Master who taught that the most profound worship should be secret and admonished "enter into thy closet, and when thou hast shut thy door, pray to thy Father which is in secret." It was he who also taught "let not thy left hand know what thy right hand doeth." Further than this, Rosicrucians have learned that organization is a rock upon which all religions have foundered and as the Fraternity is not an organization in the usual sense, it cannot be used as such to influence either government or its officials. And even when its authority or rights are challenged by a usurper, it neither requests nor uses the influence of its adherents to combat or to protest aggressively the attempt of the usurper. On the other hand, neither does it avoid nor evade a challenge, but meets issues as they arise through a constituted authority of its exoteric section without bitterness, malice or personalities.

[13] The Fraternity through the centuries has been known under various names: Hermetic, Alchemist, Essenian, Pythagorian, Paracelsian, Illuminati, Rosicrucian, the one fusing into the other; *all* forming a *whole*. *Rosicruciae* and its predecessors have little re-

---

* There are both esoteric and exoteric sections of the Grand Fraternity and these will have full consideration in due time.

** *Temple of the Rosy Cross*—Freeman B. Dowd, Edition 1901, pages 304-6.

spect for names and consider only the need of the time. The primary object of the Fraternity always has been the establishment of a Universal Brotherhood for the evolution and exaltation of the individual.

[14] Brotherhood cannot be established by enactment, by declaration nor by the power of organization. It is possible only when man, through understanding, seeks to grant the same freedom and rights to another that he seeks and demands for himself. The work of the Fraternity begins and ends with man, the individual. For as the city is to the state and the state to the nation, so is man to men and Brother to Brotherhood. As man saves himself he saves his brother and in true Brotherhood lies the path of salvation for all men and for the world. It is the dream of ages. It shall be realized only when man comes to know that *man cannot be saved by laws applied from without himself.*

[15] But it is difficult for man to believe in an ideal until he witnesses the ideal exemplified and it is almost impossible for him to understand or even to *believe* an abstract principle or Universal Law until he himself sees the law applied. Those who have really led the human race forward and have served as prophets, saviours and Messiahs to their fellowmen have exemplified man as man in his heart wishes to become. It is they who have applied the Universal Laws and principles which man, because of fear, fails to comprehend and does not dare to express. Each of the periods of advancement in all ages and among all men, regardless of color or language or race, has been initiated by the appearance upon earth of a man who by his own life and conduct manifested universal everlasting laws and principles which his fellows had not understood.

[16] It matters little whether the Awakener of the New Age is rich or poor, powerful or humble, so far as his material station in life is concerned, but it is true that the experiences of the past have disillusioned men concerning the sincerity of the teachings, and the altruism of the purpose, of kings and priests and the capitalists. The masses have followed blindly so many who proclaimed themselves their masters that they have become cynical of the motives of those who, in spite of pledges that they have made in their rise to power, subjected all to injustice and exploitation when they finally attained their coveted goal. It is because those fortunately born to power and riches have broken faith that the people have so readily turned from them these later years and have placed absolute power in the hands of men from their own rank. "Surely"

they have reasoned "this man born to poverty from humble parentage, knowing the struggle and the pain of the lowly will lead us to a new liberty." But again man found that his faith had been misplaced, for these leaders born of the masses themselves have been merciless unjust oppressors, more tyrannical than the dynasties they had displaced. And so in the New Dispensation man must learn again the lesson that he has been taught time and time again through the centuries: *justice under the law—favor to none.* This is God's great fiat in the New Dispensation. Neither political, social nor religious tyranny can retard the progress of the ever-increasing army of those who are gradually accepting and actually applying this law in their thoughts, their desires and their actions. The leader of which the masses dream is neither prince nor dictator nor is salvation to come through revolution nor through the application of radical theories but from a new concept of man in his relationship to law in its highest sense. It is true that the new "leader" may be from the ranks of the humble but he will lead man not to revolution and conquest of class by class but to a new realization of his own Manhood. "He who governs himself is greater than he who taketh the city." In these words did the elder writers describe that human creature who becomes truly a MAN. No man is fit to govern until he has first learned to govern his own passions and thus rule his own soul. The world has suffered its miseries because the power to govern has been given to men who cannot govern themselves. Countless of the multitudes over the centuries have undergone unspeakable agonies through the passions and weaknesses, the bigotry and intolerance of rulers who had no control over their own natures, who were worshipers at the throne of the Demon Self. The law inevitably works its own rewards and its own punishments and in the New Age defeat and destruction will come to those who do not obey it. In the New Age the true Brotherhood gradually will be established. It will recognize neither riches nor poverty—only the *Soul* of the *man himself.* Poverty will be relieved not through that which has been taken from others but because man under the New Dispensation, will understand and practice the laws of equity and compensation. But before he is prepared to accept and practice those principles from which his relief will come, he must experience a certain degree of suffering necessary to produce his awakening. The Brotherhood is emphatic in its interpretation of the law that THERE MUST BE A CERTAIN GROWTH AND RIPENING ERE THE FRUIT CAN BE EXPECTED. *True knowledge is the outcome of gradual growth. It concerns*

14

mind, soul and body.

[17] . . . Some foolishly think that it is possible to become a Rosicrucian through an initiation of ritual from which they may emerge with a diploma or certificate attesting membership. This is a gross misconception for Initiation is something more than taking an oath and passing through certain forms and ceremonies— no matter how imposing or awe-inspiring they may be. It is something more than a course of lectures or a study of authorities. It is something deeper and higher than intellectual culture. *It is the knowing of truth.* It has been well said that not every man can become adept at anything nor is it possible for every man to become a Rosicrucian. He must have a conscious and abiding belief in his own immortality; a hunger and thirst for the unknown; a *feeling of rapture* at the very idea of mystery and Brotherhood. Among such as these initiation may be accomplished with advantage to self and to mankind for in *Rosicruciaes'* Temple they that eat are filled and they that drink thirst no more. Under its protection are found teachers, guides and brothers. We are children of the "shadow" and though often we may not see the way clearly through tear-dimmed eyes yet as we cry out in anguish, "Not my will Father but Thine own be done" the "shadow" reveals its mystery and departs leaving the heart chastened and yet lightened through an increase of knowledge and of peace. Men are cast down. That they may go higher and thus alternately cast down and exalted they are prepared to meet the changes of the mundane life. No stoic, agnostic or egotist can become a Rosicrucian for Initiation requires an intensified *feeling.* Without this, no initiation could possibly impart that baptism to the spirit which gives birth to new or dormant energies; nor without it could the soul germ be awakened to a higher life. Where Will reigns over all and matter becomes transmutable the law may be understood and applied and the Brotherhood of the New Age established.

[18] The Rosicrucians ever have been the Apostles of Peace, Freedom and Brotherhood. Washington, nobly knighted and anointed by the brethren, proved true to his trust. His memory is a symbol of the Universal Fellowship of Man in Freedom. Washington sought peace. It was only as a last recourse that he consented to head the Continental army and as its commander he sacrificed no property nor lives except directly in the cause to which he was consecrated. France too sought to gain her freedom through the overthrow of an unworthy king. Those who were the leaders of the movement for freedom in France were imbued

with the spirit of hate and fear and the lust for blood. So great was the unnecessary destruction of property and shedding of royalist blood that it almost could be said that this was the real motive that animated its leaders rather than that of Fraternity, Equality and Peace. France paid dearly for her liberty. Under the leadership of Washington, a true leader of the people, well trained in the Great Brotherhood, it was vastly different. He had no vain personal ambition, he sought only the freedom and the welfare of those whom he called his people. The Brotherhood has always taught and still teaches that *nothing can be gained by the unnecessary destruction of anything useful*. That which is destroyed *must be replaced* and though he win, the victor who ignores this law will be the loser. Since the days of Washington, the Brother and Robespierre, the Revolutionist, strange as it may seem, almost all the battles for freedom have become revolutions of blood. For those who have instigated them have been motivated by bitterness and selfish thirst for power rather than by love of man.

[19] There is but one lawful object in the life of man—*freedom—the right to live under the Law without interference*. For this objective he may and should fight but without hatred and malice. If in gaining his freedom he himself disobeys this law, then in the reaction of the law once more will he become a slave. Washington, an Apostle of Brotherhood, fought because there was no other way to gain freedom for his people. But when that objective was gained with as little loss and destruction as possible, he ceased his warfare since he was fighting only for a cause without thought or intent of self-gain or personal glorification. "More blood—more blood to wash the records of the poor man's wrong from the history of ages" was the cry of the revolution in France. The abused and degraded masses tore power from the hands of their rulers. But vindictive, thirsting for blood, drunk with the freedom for which they were not prepared, they gave themselves to the leadership of those who cried for blood and more blood. The law inevitably produced the reaction. The leaders themselves died by the axe they had wielded and once more slaves that had tasted freedom only to abuse it, became slaves again.

[20] He who is motivated by the passions of vengeance and hatred may attain his objective, but no matter how just his cause, the fruits of his victory will be taken from him. This is the law of action and reaction. "Vengeance is mine," sayeth the Lord. Robespierre sought freedom for a people, but his nature was filled with hatred and bitterness and revenge. He was dominated by the hatred of a

class and he destroyed as an avenging angel. He destroyed because he hated a class more than he loved a people. A demon within him fed on his passions and since he had given reign to his evil propensities, it carried him into responsibility for great wrongs and terrible destruction until finally the reaction of the law began to function and "unto him was done even as he had done unto others." So until men comprehend and only as their actions are governed by motives of love, may they demand justice within the law without its reaction.

[21] To America, the land of promise, the new world of the prophecy in which was to be found freedom and Brotherhood, men came to free themselves from persecution and tyranny. Yet, strange as it is, those who came to this promised land and settled it because persecution had driven them from their own lands, became themselves narrow, bigoted, cruel, superstitious, subjecting those who would not agree with them to even greater persecution and suffering than they themselves had escaped from. It is stranger still that a people who fought long years for liberty from the rule of a foreign king should submit to the rule of racketeers, gangsters, crooked politicians and profiteers. But *even now* the law is functioning and where the leavening is occurring, the fermentation of the wine must come before the clarification. The LAW *is* and regardless of how man may evade it, inevitably the reaction MUST set in. In the universal depression which has seemingly fallen on the just and unjust alike, the law is being satisfied through the suffering of those who were guilty of its evasions, either through omission or commission. That man who has submitted without protest to the conditions from which came the violation of his rights and those of the fellowmen of his nation, suffers that he may be awakened; that his voice may be heard. Then will begin the functioning of the Law of the New Age. The unjust, the decadent and those who seek to retard the operation of the Law will be known no longer and so will begin the era of the Brotherhood of Man.

[22] Washington was consecrated as a deliverer of his people and it was his destiny to lead his people to a new concept of independence and of liberty. Washington was true to his sacred mission as deliverer. He won the conflict that he himself must have faced within his inner being as to whether to live and to lead in the interest of the rights of his fellowmen or to crown himself and rule over others for his own glorification. It is possible for those *destined* to lead the people of the new era to fail, because even though God or the Law ordains a man for the performance of some

great function, that man still has *free will* and though God ordains he does not command. In the being of every man there are two creatures, one noble and aspiring, the other selfish and earthly. One speaks with the voice of love and seeks the good of all humanity. The other speaks with the voice of self and seeks only its own benefit and advantage. There is a constant conflict between these two forces in the heart of man. Irrespective of how high he may climb on the ladder of his own evolution there is always the possibility that he may fall. The Great Master expressed this danger for he admonished "when ye stand take heed lest ye fall." Lucifer fell from the second highest place in "heaven" to the lowest depths. We may accept this fall as a symbol of a lesson all men, no matter how great, may profit by. It is because of the recognition of this possibility that there never has been written a history of living Rosicrucians. It is a law in the August Fraternity that no man may disgrace the Grand Fraternity by his misdeeds and consequently it is a law that none except the exoteric workers shall become known as Rosicrucians until after their work is done and there is no longer any possibility of error on their part. For the same reason no Rosicrucian may claim to be such and he who proclaims himself a Rosicrucian is not what he pretends to be. "They who know do not talk, they who talk do not know." Beware of pretenders.

[23] But fortunately for the new world Washington did not fail in his mission and the Second Epoch was passed safely and men learned for the first time the taste of freedom. They knew little of self-control and nothing of self-government and to most, freedom and liberty meant license. Man learns but gradually and hence the depression—a reaction of the law resulting from man's failure to properly govern himself as a Free Man. It has been a necessary experience and keen as is the suffering it has occasioned it has compelled a recognition of that to which man previously had blinded his eyes. Now the New Dispensation is at hand. We are at the beginning of the Third Epoch. The divine law is functioning and through it perhaps there will rise to express it another Washington as the anointed one. THE LAW WILL PROVIDE. Not all will be saved for *there is a loss in every activity*. Weaklings, regardless of their station in life, will continue to refuse to accept the law. They will, as ever, depend upon others rather than themselves and since they will not BECOME MEN the unceasing grinding of the mills of the gods will eliminate them from the field of action. This is the law. It is not unjust. Each one is given the opportunity to

know and to obey the law; to work in harmony with it and to secure its protection. Those who refuse to obey the law will eliminate themselves by the inharmony *which they themselves create.* In the New Age each man must be responsible for his own accounting—no man can vicariously intercede. St. John in his revelations foresaw this and spoke of the saving of the "forty and four thousand," a number highly symbolical.

[24] The post-war era of gold and plenty and the depression which followed it both have brought out vividly man's every weakness. They have shown that cruelty, craftiness, debasement, may occur either in the palace or in the gutter. It is shown that unjust as may be the emperor or the capitalistic feudal lord; the toiler and worker also may be unjust when wielding power over his fellow-man. It was necessary that this lesson be learned that man might recognize that it is not the station, environment nor the individual circumstance that produces a leader. He is beginning to realize that he must turn for leadership to those men, rich or poor, who KNOW the Law and will apply it. The man who accepts the Law and does his utmost to LIVE that law, will have its protection, and although he be thrown among thieves and outcasts, he will be overshadowed and protected as was Daniel in the lion's den. Once this is comprehended men will no longer be so concerned with the reformation of other men. Their chief concern will be to *reform themselves.* They will realize more and more that revolutions, shedding of blood, destruction of property do not gain their rights but lead them away from their direct objective except when it is countenanced by the Law. From the beginning the Fraternity of the Rosy Cross has been consistently engaged in trying to bring about a better understanding among men, and in the attempt, to eradicate through the education of the classes and the masses those abuses which have made nations charnel houses. It has been the effort of the Fraternity through the ages to inculcate the Law so that all might understand it and come under its protection.

[25] There are *many* phases, branches and degrees in the Grand Fraternity—the Rosy Cross*, but only three of these concern us here. The Rosicrucian Order, the Rosicrucian Brotherhood, the Fraternity of the Rosicrucians. As a direct outgrowth of the activities of George Lippard, Freeman B. Dowd, a Grand Master of the Fraternity, induced his appointed successor, Dr. Edward H. Brown,

---

* Other phases of the Great Work will be dealt with in detail in a publication to follow the present one in which will be given a partial history, together with documents, establishing the Grand Fraternity in America.

to define these terms. The *Rosicrucian Order* or *Order of the Rose* or *Rosy Cross* is composed of that body of men and women who, though more or less interested in the philosophy of the Fraternity, nevertheless are particularily concerned with the establishment of "lodges" of a formal nature wherein may be taught through the conferring of degrees, through lectures and dissertations, a better understanding of the law of relationship between man and man. It is the desire of the order to improve the condition of man, to advance the establishment of the Brotherhood of man, to bring about an understanding of law and to aid in effecting its application in the world of men. Those seeking membership are not required to subscribe to the tenets of the Grand Fraternity nor will they be required to delve deeply into the ancient mysteries nor to undergo arduous training. *The Rosicrucian Brotherhood* or *Brotherhood of the Rosy Cross* is a body of men and women who are not interested in ceremonials but who are deeply interested in the philosophy of the ancient mysteries. In this Brotherhood members subscribe to the tenets of the Fraternity and seek to aid in establishing a Universal Brotherhood through an understanding and application of the laws taught by the Fraternity. The members of the Brotherhood are willing to make such sacrifices as may be necessary to bring about the Brotherhood and Freedom of man. It is not necessary to become a member of any lodge to belong to the Brotherhood but allegiance to the Supreme Body is required. The members may or may not be known to each other. Two may live next door to each other without either knowing that the other is a member unless through the stress of circumstances, they become acquainted. They are silent; they have at heart a love of their fellowmen and they are workers in the "vineyard of the Lord." The FRATERNITY OF THE ROSICRUCIANS or the *Fraternitas Rosae Crucis* is the highest tribunal. Few members of this body ever become known either to the world or to the general membership. Its members are those whose very Souls are in the Great Work. These are willing to make any sacrifice required and are ready and willing to undergo complete training as outlined by the ancient Fraternity. These members enroll for life and they seek no greater glory than to become God-like—MEN. From these are chosen the members of the various Councils and the future Grand Master and the Hierarchs. While they themselves remain unknown, it is given to them to know those who may be in the various branches and bodies of the Fraternity. They seek to obey to the full the behests of the Great Master, and, following his admonition they worship alone and in silence. They may be known only by their unpretending good works; by the kindness of their hearts and the justice of their decisions. All may aspire to this lofty association but few attain because of pride, the thirst for glory, love of display, carelessness of speech, lack of will, fear of the opinion of others, sensitiveness to censure and criticism and lack of concentration of purpose. These are but three of the grades of the Great Work of the Grand Fraternity, but there is a phase or grade of the work suitable to all men who SEEK TO BETTER THEMSELVES but not at the expense of another.

[26] The Grand Fraternity has passed through innumerable changes within the past ten centuries. Not always was it known as the Rosy Cross. It has been known as the Egyptian Initiation, Gnostic Priesthood, the Essenian Order, the Order of the Magi, Heberites, Hermetic, Alchemist, Platonist and Paracelsian. The name by which it has been known has harmonized with the needs of the time and as the needs of humanity have changed so has the phase and the name of the Great Work. With each change the experience and teachings of the past were fused into those of the new era. In 1612 a convocation was convened at Frankfort-on-the-Main, in Germany. Among those who answered the call were the representatives of members of many of the ancient orders, in some of which there remained but few active members. The Gnostic Fathers were in attendance; adepts of the Hermetic and Alchemistic Orders; learned of the Platonists; modern Gnostics; active members of the Paracelsian school and representatives of other of the ancient bodies. These delegates possessed authority from their respective Fraternities or "schools" to consider and deal with all the problems with which they were confronted. The fiat had gone forth to all that the time prophesied by Paracelsus to form and act as a concerted movement had come. As an outcome of the convocation there was brought into union all the activities of the true schools and at the instance of Andrea the new union was given a mystical name with full provision for secrecy so that no member active in it would be known to the world. The name that was adopted was the Fraternitas Rosae Crucis or the Fraternity of the Rosy Cross. Its principle as applied to the relationships between the various bodies that it had absorbed was expressed in the words "one in all, all in one." Each fraternal member was individual and yet of the union. Its expression was "union in diversity."

[27] During the seventeenth century there was but one supreme body and its jurisdiction was through a Council of Three and a

Council of Seven.   Under the Council of Seven was a Supreme Chief who was elected by the Council of Seven and under him there served a Chief from each country.   Beginning with the eighteenth century jurisdictions were separated and while the Council of Seven continued to function, its membership comprised the Supreme Chiefs of every country, each of whom had absolute authority and jurisdiction in his own country.   With the entry of America into the Council, a change was made in the practice and each Supreme Chief or Supreme Grand Master, as he was thenceforth known, was given irrevocable authority *to select* his own successor, in recognition of the fact that only he could know which brother had attained the *right* of succession to the exalted position.   At this time a Council of Three was constituted within the grand body consisting of the Supreme Grand Master and the two members within the Fraternity most advanced and best prepared in the Work.   Two members always were selected by the Supreme Grand Master immediately upon his taking his authority and from the two he selected his successor.

[28] The first American Conclave of the Supreme Council of Nine was convened in the City of Philadelphia in 1773 instead of 1777 as had been intended.   The earlier date was chosen because of the increasing friction between England and the colonies and the consequent necessity for final instructions to those of the Brotherhood who were to take part in the great struggle which it was known would occur.   The conclave was a Supreme Council of the World for the American Supreme Grand Lodge had not yet been created. The year of 1848 stands forth in the history of the Rosy Cross. It was in that year that the Supreme Council of the World determined to remove the seat of the SEE of the Supreme Council of the World from the old world to the new; and that the Brotherhood within the United States and its possessions be permitted to form its own Supreme Grand Lodge with an American as Supreme Grand Master.   It was in this year also that the selection was made by the Supreme Council of Abraham Lincoln as the "anointed one" to carry further the work for freedom to which Washington also had been consecrated.   It was also determined in this year that after the initiation in the mother lodge of Frankfort-on-the-Main of the one who would become Supreme Grand Master of the Fraternity that that lodge would be closed for ever.   The year of 1884 is of historical importance in the work of the Rosy Cross, for it was in that year that Freeman B. Dowd, after having taken his seat as the Supreme Grand Master of the Rosy Cross following the death

of Dr. P. B. Randolph, the first Supreme Grand Master in America, established, by instruction of Count Guinotti, the Supreme Grand Temple of the Rosy Cross of the World in Philadelphia as a direct and authentic continuation of the Rosicrucian movement which was first established by the *Council of Seven* in the City of Philadelphia in 1773 and which had never ceased to function as a supreme body of authority.

R. SWINBURNE CLYMER.

THE MEETING OF THE
COUNCIL OF SEVEN
OF THE
BROTHERHOOD OF THE ROSY CROSS
The First World Parliament

There was a night, when a band of earnest men, who believed that God might be adored and man be loved without the medium of church or creed, assembled in the solitudes of a mountain cavern.[1] They were but few in number, and yet it seemed as if all the nations of the earth had sent their representatives to this secret Congress of Brotherhood,[2] this obscure Parliament of Love.

History, or that fabric of falsehood,[3] which is promulgated to the world as history, does not record the names of these men, who formed the little band; and yet, their deliberations went forth from that mountain cavern over all the world, like the voice of a Regenerating Angel.

The fair-haired German was there; and by his side the Spaniard, with his bronzed cheek, and eye of fire. There, the Italian, full of the ancient glory of his land, and the Frenchman, with his story of Protestant and Catholic wars. The Swede, the Dane, the Hungarian, and the Turk,—all were mingled in that band. Even the far land of the New World was represented there in the person of a Colonist, fresh from the witchcraft murders of New England.

These men, grouping round a rock which started from the cavern floor, talked with each other in low, earnest tones. A single torch, inserted in the crevice of the rock, gave its faint light to the scene, and dimly revealed their various costumes, and the passions as various, which flitted over each face.

Near that rock, a solitary figure towered erect, his face and form concealed by a dark robe.

While all the others conversed in agitated whispers, he alone was silent.

Not a gesture betrayed his emotion, nor indicated that he was in truth anything but a dumb image of wood or stone.

There was but one in the little band who knew his name.

Wherefore this assemblage in the mountain cavern of Germany, at dead of night, by the faint ray of a solitary torch?

Wherefore these signs, by which the various persons recognized each other? And what meant that password in the ancient Hebrew tongue, which echoes round the place until the gloomy arches seemed agitated into voice by the sound?

It will be remembered, that this meeting took place when the first quarter of the seventeenth century was near its close.

The German, with his fair hair and blue eyes, arose:

"Reformations are in vain for my fatherland.[4] A new Luther must arise and work out a broader and bolder Reformation. The last has but substituted one creed for another—Germany festers with the unburied corpses of those who have been slain in the war of Creeds. The Reformation only agitated the atmosphere in which Kings and Priests swelter into bloated power. It left the Poor where it found them—there, under the hoofs of Priest and King, doomed to dig and die, whether a Pope or a Synod reigns. Earth calls to God for a new Reformation, which shall overlook the world, as with the eye of God himself, and behold in God but the common Father of all mankind; in nations and races, however divided or styled, but a common family of Brothers."

As the German took his seat upon a ledge of rock, near the central rock, a murmur of deep emphasis filled the cavern.

Then, one by one, the members of the little band arose, and spoke the thought of their souls freely, and with no fear upon their faces.

The Spaniard rose—

"In Spain exists the Inquisition—"

As if these words comprised all that man can know of degradation, all that Priests can inflict, or Kings contrive, in the form of Murder, he said no more.[5]

Next the Frenchman—

"St. Bartholomew's corpses have not yet moulded into dust," he said, and was silent.

After he had ceased, an Irishman arose. He had no word to utter, or perchance his heart was too full for words. He laid upon the rock, in the rays of the light, some leaves of withered shamrock, and a broken harp. The withered leaves and broken harp were stained with blood.

Without a word, the Irishman glided into the shadows again. Then the voice of the Englishman was heard—

"Some time ago there was a war in my native land. The People,

25

that vulgar race, whose life is comprised in three words—we are born, we suffer, we die! The People, I say, came up bravely to that war, and spoke with an ominous murmur to an anointed King, telling him in their rude way, that he was but a man. That, forgetting his Manhood in his Kingship, he had committed murders enough to have hurled a thousand men to the scaffold. Therefore, said the People, King as you are, with the royal blood of twenty generations in your veins, with the anointing oil of all the Priests in the land upon your brow, you must die.

"They put their King to death upon the scaffold, and said in the face of God and Man—'We will have no more to do with Kings. They have had the world long enough for their Murder ground— long enough have they set men at one another's throats, and turned the Image of God into an engine of carnage.' This was a brave thing, which the English People said, but the time was not yet come: they had not yet learned the great lesson of our order. First, Union; then Freedom; and last Brotherhood.[6]

"They could not yet recognize in God, but a loving Father of all mankind, nor in nations and races, but a family of Brothers.

"Therefore, after having put their King to death, and buried the word 'King,' with his headless body, they became the slaves of Faction. They quarreled about creeds and forms, leaving the great fact of all Truth—BROTHERHOOD AMONG MEN—a dumb and mangled thing beneath their bloody feet.[7]

"At this time, a bold Son of the People cast his eyes about him, and saw the danger of his brethren. He saw the word 'King' start into life again from the headless body of Charles the First—he saw the People once more kneeling in their blood, under the iron feet of Power.

"He determined to save his race, but, alas! pity us, good Lord, for we are weak!—he could think of no better way of saving his people from the name of 'King,' than by usurping the Power without the Name.[8]

"Therefore, the Lord delivered him not into the hands of his enemies, but to the remorse of his own soul. Delivered his great heart to the terror of the Assassin's steel—delivered his giant intellect, blinded and bound, like the Samson of old, to that terror which fears a shadow, and trembles at a sound.

"At last he died, and England, forgetful of the blood which had been shed to achieve her freedom—forgetful even of the greatness of that Brewer, who had made the name of Protector nobler than the name of Emperor—England, I say, forgetful of the brave men who had died, by tens of thousands, to redeem her from the name of King—England rushed to the grave of Charles the First, and took the crown from his fleshless skull, and put it on the head of Charles the Second, and hailed him—'King.' [9]

"Yes, my brothers, Charles the Second is King of England now, and while he reigns, there is a headless trunk amid the offal of the ditch, there is a bleeding head nailed up to scorn, upon the gates of London. That headless trunk, and that bleeding heart, once embodied the Soul of Oliver Cromwell."

The Englishman could say no more. Charles the Second on the Throne, and Oliver Cromwell's body cast forth to feed the hunger of dogs, Oliver Cromwell's head nailed up to the gate of London— it was enough.

The Representatives of the Nations uttered a groan for fallen England. Then, one by one, these men gathered from the quarters of the globe—assembled at the mandate of some Invisible Chief, or by the watchword of a universal brotherhood—arose and told, in various ways, in every tongue, the same story.

Kings everywhere, Priests everywhere, and everywhere slaves.[10]

It was a horrible catalog of enormities, which fell from the lips of these brethren.

Indeed, it seemed as if the World—its men and women, its little children, and its babes unborn—had been given up by some ferocious Destiny into the hands of Superstition and Murder.

The Turk, the Arab, the Hindoo, and the Swede, all told the same story in various forms. In every land a King, and for the People nothing but chains and graves.

There was a black man in the throng; from his voice and manner it appeared that he had received the education of the white race.

The story that the black man told, was of petty Kings, on the soil of Africa, selling the flesh and blood of Africa to eternal bondage in a New World. A bondage that had no parallel in the history of crime, for under the name of Servitude, it comprised Murder, Incest, Blasphemy.

As the word "New World" fell from the black man's lips, a shudder agitated the throng.

"Slavery in the New World!" cried the German—"Alas! Alas! then God has indeed given the earth into the power of Satan——"

"Do not blaspheme," said the voice of the aged Swede— "The New World is the last altar of Brotherhood left on the surface of a desolated globe. We have looked to the East for Light—it will come from the East; but in the West that Light will reveal to us

27

the perfect image of human brotherhood."

At this word the representatives from the New World arose. Every one was silent; they all gazed upon his rugged features and backwoodsman attire with an absorbing interest.

"The New World is the last altar of human Brotherhood!" he said, echoing the words of the aged Swede—"There was a band of friendless exiles, driven from the shores of England by the lash of persecution. They sought a Home and an Altar in the forests of the New World. They landed one day, on a Rock which they called Plymouth, and the red men of the woods bade the wanderers welcome. Brothers, this was not many years ago, and yet I stand among you, an exile and an outcast from the New World—"

"An exile and an outcast from the New World!" His words were echoed on every side.

"He has committed some horrible crime—" and the aged Swede shrunk from the side of the Colonist.

"Yes, I was guilty of crime—a horrible crime. I could not believe in my neighbor's creed. I could not think that Murder was any the less Murder, because it was done by grim Priests, in the name of God, and the victims were old men and defenseless women. Yes, yes—I have stood upon the soil of the New World, and seen men given up to the cord and scaffold, because they could not believe in an Orthodox Protestant creed—

—"Even as I, a Spaniard, have seen them racked and burnt in the Act of Faith on an Inquisition!"

"But I have seen that Image which we love in a Wife, reverence in a Sister, adored in a Mother—I have seen the Image of Woman lashed naked through the streets, amid the jeers and prayers of cadaverous Priests, who saw the blood start from the quivering flesh, and shouted, 'Scorn to the Heretic, Praise to our God.' This on the soil of the New World—this in the land which God hath set apart as the most sacred altar of human Brotherhood!"[11]

Bathed in tears and blushed, the American crouched into a seat. One groan quivered from the hearts of the listeners.

"We all looked to the New World for Light, and lo! we have it, but it is the light from the flame of persecution, the red blaze which bigotry has stolen from the fires of hell."

From the verge of the circle which the brothers formed, as they clustered around the light, a tall form advanced. It was a man clad in a blanket, with a wampum belt wound about his waist; a man of aquiline nose and high cheek-bone, eyes like sparks of flame, and

28

skin that resembled the deep red of autumnal leaves.

"I am an Indian," he said in a guttural tone. "But the language of your Brotherhood has become my language. The altar at which you worship is also mine. I am an Indian. Twenty winters ago I dwelt among my people beside the river which flows from the forest to the sea. Our numbers were as the leaves in the forest, as the sands by the shore. From the wood to the river, extended our wigwams, thick as the birds in the sky, when the sun is low. The White Man came; he was attired in black. There was a Cross upon his Breast. He taught my People a new Religion; he built his temple in our midst. The Great Spirit whom we had seen in the sky, we now behold in a Cross, and worshipped in the form of a Silver Cup. And yet his Religion made the heart warm within us, for he spoke of a Great Being, who had come from the sky, so that he might suffer among men, and die despised and scorned upon a tree, in order that all men might love one another. It was a beautiful Religion, and we loved it. Our warriors knelt at the foot of the Cross—our maidens placed the Cross upon their bosoms, and set it, bound with flowers, amid the folds of their raven hair. We loved the Religion, and the men in the dark robe who taught us to love it, grew white-haired among us.

"One morning in summer, as we were gathered in the temple near the river shore—as the old man lifted the Cup on high, while our nation knelt at his feet—a bullet pierced his brain. He fell at the foot of the Cross. A red blaze streamed through every window—there was a sound like a hundred thunder-claps in the air. There were a hundred dead bodies on the floor of the temple.*

"The grass without the temple was burdened with the dead—the river, near us, grew red with blood on every wave.

"From the rocks on the opposite shore, streamed one incessant sheet of flame.

"Evening came at last. The sun was setting. I was the only living man, and I stood alone amid the harvest of death."

A cry of horror pervaded the cavern.

"Who was it that did this deed? Who were the murderers—the savages of other tribes, your foes among the red men?"

"They were white men who did the deed. They believed in the same being whom the man in the dark robe taught us to love."

"Wherefore this murder?" asked the Swede.

---

* Father Ralle. His mission was among the Norridgewocks along the Kennebec river. A massacre of Christian converts by Christian soldiers. The shedding of blood without even a shred of cause.

29

"These white men, who came upon us as we knelt in prayer, and shot us down, and stabbed us, as we rose upon the river's wave, and pierced our skulls as we crept into the bushes—these white men believed in the same Cross in which the old man believed, but—" a sad smile stole over the red features of the Indian—"they only believed in the Cross as it was written in the Book—while the old man believed in it as it was carved in wood or sculptured in stone. Therefore they murdered us."

There was a pause of stillness, unbroken by a sound.

"Brothers," cried the Indian, "I come to you in the name of the Red Man. We melt away before the white race like snow before the flame. They kill us with the sword, they poison us with fire-water, they sweep us away with the plague. Help, or we are dead."

The appeal of the Red Man touched every heart.

An Italian, with every line of his animated countenance stamped by thought and endurance, next rose.

"Italy," he exclaimed, "is palsied by a Nightmare, which crouches upon her breast, and slowly drinks the blood from her heart. The Nightmare changes its form every instant—now it is a Priest, now it is a King; now the Priest and King, combined in one, realize the idea of an Incarnate Devil. Help for Italy, ere the last drop of her blood is spent!"

Then by the side of the Italian appeared the dark figure of a Jesuit. Every eye shuddered to behold him there—all wondered why he had dared intrude upon this band of brothers—not a man but shrunk away from him, afraid of the very folds of his dark robe.

"Help for the Catholic Church," he exclaimed. "Help, Brothers of Love, for that Church which once overspread the earth, and sheltered all men under the wings of her Divine Unity! She now lies bleeding in the hands of Princes who call themselves Priests, of Murderers who call themselves Pastors!"

The smile that had agitated every face when he commenced, died away in the look of sympathy as his last word fell on their ears. They extended their hands; they encircled him.

"There is hope for man, when the Jesuit invokes the aid of Brotherhood in behalf of the Church!"

And all the while that solitary figure stood veiled—speechless and motionless—near the rock; alone amid the throng.

The Rosy Cross

Only one in the secret band knew his name and history.[11] The time now came for that man to speak.

He came from the shadows, and stood disclosed in the light, his tall form, arrayed in the gray garb of a peasant, standing distinctly into view. His features were darkened by exposure to the wind and sun; his large brow projected over eyes which shone steadily with an exchanging lustre. Those eyes shone into every heart, and all the brethren in the cavern felt that a Great Soul was embodied in their light.

This man, in the coarse peasant garb, leaned one hand—cramped and knotted by toil—upon the shoulder of the veiled form. In a voice harsh and abrupt, he began to speak.

He spoke of a Secret Order extending over all the earth, and dating its origin back to that dim time, when history becomes a fable, and chronology a shadow.[12] Of the rites, symbols and customs of the Order—which spoke to the heart, through the eye, and formed a universal language, intelligible to brothers of every race and clime. Of the most sacred sign of the Order, which was written on the pyramids of Egypt, and the Monuments of Mexico, and stamped upon the dumb stone and mortar of past ages, in every quarter of the globe—the most sacred sign, a Cross placed upon a globe, and lighted by the rays of a rising sun, and therefore called the red or Rosy Cross.

This Cross, placed upon a dark globe, with the dawn breaking over its darkness, was the emblem of the great purpose of the Order—the regeneration of the millions of mankind, by three great ideas, Union, Freedom, Brotherhood.

The Globe was a symbol of Union; the Light, breaking upon it from the darkness, an emblem of Freedom. The Cross standing above upon the globe, and blushing into radiance in the fast coming light, was a type of *Brotherhood*.

This Order was known among men—known only in vague supposition and Unaccredited tradition—as the *Brotherhood of the Rosy Cross*.

As the brother in the peasant garb went on, his harsh voice became melodious, his manner, no longer hesitating, grew firm and bold. He traced the history of the Brotherhood from the far gone ages, down to the present time.[13] In language vivid and eloquent, he pictured the elaborate ceremonial, the giant organization, the fascinating mystery, which characterized the Order, and made its

31

power felt over the world, in all times, like the hand of God.

"And yet, with all this Power—these Symbols, that form a common language for Brothers of all nations, these rites, that elevate with their beauty and bewilder with their mystery—with all its power, felt through all ages, over all the world, like the hand of God, behold the degradation of mankind. In vain our labor, in vain the labors of our fathers. In vain this tremendous organization, in vain the universal language, the rites, the symbols—all in vain. Man still bleeds under the feet of Priest and King—the world is still given up to Satan. Even that holiest name, which we have written upon our banner, embalmed in our hearts, consecrated with the baptism of our tears—even *'Brotherhood'* has fallen prostrate,[14] afraid of the darkness which broods over the earth, trampled into dust by the iron feet of Evil."

These words thrilled through the cavern, and a breathless stillness fell upon every tongue. Faces, wet with tears, that glittered in the dim light, attested the truth, the power of the speaker's words.

Still resting his knotted hand upon the shoulder of the unknown, the peasant in the grey garb continued:

"But the contest is not yet over. *'Brotherhood'* is clouded by mists of blood-red smoke, but it is Divine, it is Eternal, it will live when the stars have faded from the sky. For it is of God, and therefore cannot die.

"But we must embody the idea of *'Brotherhood'* not only in rites and symbols, but in such a form that the meanest of earth's trodden children may behold it and love it.

"Do you hear me, my brethren?

"This idea of Brotherhood, nay, this Eternal Fact, this deathless manifestation of God, must be embodied into a form, that will speak to the hearts of men, and through their hearts regenerate the world."

"Do this," cried the Swede, "and Kings and Priests exist no longer." [15]

Every face was lifted in earnest hope to the visage of the speaker, and a murmur filled the cavern, a murmur swelled by many tongues, but with only one meaning.

"Let the Divine Truth of Brotherhood be embodied in a form that will speak at once to the hearts of men, and our work is done. Man will indeed be free; there will exist no longer on the face of the globe, either a Lord or a Slave, to blaspheme, by their existence, the goodness of *our Father.*"

"But how shall the idea be embodied? In what form shall we personify the holy Truth?"

"Listen, my brothers, and I will tell you. We will embody this idea in the history of some individual life, whose every word shall melt the souls of men into tenderness and love. Shall we take the idea of some great philosopher—some of those weird sages of the ancient time, who surveyed the world from the casement of their cells, and reasoned boldly upon Man, but could not feel for him? Shall we summon Pythagoras—or Plato—or even that bravest and most manful of them all—Socrates? Ah, I see the smile steal over your faces—I hear your murmurs. What have Philosophers to do with the millions of mankind? Have they suffered, any moment of their lives, that stern Martyrdom which is ever the lot of the Poor Man, from his birth to his death—the Martyrdom of Poverty, that has no couch for its tired head, but in the grave; the Martyrdom of Toil, that is without a Hope in this world or the next. Have these Philosophers drunk of the poor man's cup; have they wept with him in his desolate home; have they measured his anguish, or sounded the depths of his immeasurable Despair?

"Away then with Philosophers. Cold reasoners, shrouding themselves in the mountain cloud of sophistry; they never descend to the plain, and feel with the millions who are only born to be trampled and to die.

"The world does not demand abstractions. It calls, even from the kennel of its degradation, it calls for some great Heart, to feel for its despair, and win it tenderly into light and love once more.

"Shall we embody this Idea of Brotherhood in the life of some Priest, or tell the world how lovely it looks, how wonderful and sublime in the life of some King? As well embody the Idea of Heaven in the image of a Satyr, or personify the angel-tenderness of childhood in the dusk countenance of Satan!

"No—away with Priests and Kings—away with all like these who *do not live in the same world* with the millions of mankind.

"But we will give this idea shape, color and voice. We will embody the principle of Brotherhood in the life of a Mechanic."

His words were followed by a breathless stillness; and then the murmur rose—"Where will you find a Mechanic, who has risen from the hut of the poor man into the light of fame?"

"In the life of a worker, toiling with the workers of the human race, a Son of the Poor, living and dying for the Poor. Listen, my brothers, and do not treat with scorn my crude Legend of other days. But I will tell to you the story of the Mechanic whom you

33

seek, the son of the Poor whom you desire.

"One day—in the ages long ago—the Son of a Carpenter looked out from the window of his father's workshop, and beheld his brothers and sisters, the Poor, trodden down under the gathered infamies of four thousand years. His garments were very rude; clad like a child of the People, he wiped the laborer's sweat from his brow, and from that workshop window, he cast his eyes over a world in darkness and in chains. A Fire that was of God suddenly lighted up his eyes; that forehead, damp with the sweat of toil, became radiant with a Thought. His lips inclosed, and he uttered the travail of his soul in these brief words—'Over all the earth, one sound swells up to God. It is the groan of the Poor man, who has no joy in this world, and no hope in the next.'

"Then, as if the voice from God had penetrated his soul, the Son of the Carpenter laid aside the tools of his father's craft, and, clad as he was, in the coarse garb of labor, yet with a Thought shining over his brow, went forth into the world, and said to the Poor, as he met them on the highway, or saw them bending under the hot sun, in the rich man's fields, or beheld their wan faces from the windows of the prison, 'Brother,' there is a God in heaven! He marks the sparrow's fall—think you, then, that He looks unheedingly upon the anguish of his children, the Poor, who bear his image, and have every one of them a ray of his Eternity in their hearts?'"

"Such words as these, thrilling from the lips of a Carpenter's Son, stirred the hearts of the Poor. They followed the young man by thousands; now by the shore, now on the slope of the mountain side, now in the desert woods, he talked to them, as much with his radiant forehead and calm deep eyes, as with his voice; and he always ended his teachings with a word like this—'God is our Father, and all men are his children.'

"I might spend the hours of this silent night, in telling you how this Son of the Carpenter dwelt with the Poor—shared the crust of the Poor—wept with the Poor—lived for the Poor, and died for the Poor. As for the Rich Man, whether he appeared in the form of the Priest, or as a King, the Son of the Carpenter only spoke of him with pity, with reproach, with scorn. His mission was for the Poor.[16] And without arms, without Priests, clad only in his humble garb, he spoke to the Poor of his native land, and his voice moved the earth like the pulsations of the Heart of God.

"He died—at last, after a brief mission of three years—he died; I need not tell you how!

"What death is reserved for those who endeavor with a single heart to do good to Man? Not the death of the Pampered Priest, who, reclining on silken couches—embosomed in the chambers of a Palace—looks, with sorrow too deep for tears, upon the rich viands and the genial wines, which he cannot take with him to the grave. Not the death of the Conqueror, who makes himself a couch of the bodies of the slain, and expires most royally—a tiger clad in glossy fur, crouching upon his victims and tearing them with his fangs, as he dies.

"No! But the death of the Felon, nailed to an abhorred tree, which towered alone and hideous, upon the heights of a craggy steep, with the black sky above it, and the dark mass of countless spectators around and beneath it.

"This was the death of the Son of the Carpenter, who had said to Man, that Religion consisted not in palaces or jails, nor in Priests and Kings, nor in churches, or costly ceremonials, but—mark the simplicity of the Carpenter's Son—in *Loving one another.*

"O, that I could paint to you the radiant forehead and earnest eyes of this Carpenter's Son, and show him to you as he lived among men, their Brother: clad like themselves, their Friend: for he said to them, *God is our Father.*

"But he has been dead many centuries. Behold him, not as he walked the sands of his native land, but as he is!"

He swept the cloak aside, which enveloped the limbs of the unknown. The cavern echoed with a cry of amazement and terror.

For there, very near the light, towered the Leaden Image, whose forehead stamped with despair, and motionless eyes full of unutterable anguish; the form clad in the garments of toil, seemed to imprison a Living Soul.

It was the Image of the Imprisoned Jesus.

"This is what Priest and King [and the mass who for centuries have followed a dead form and wholly missed the *spirit*] have made of the poor and beautiful spirit of the Carpenter's Son! They have robbed man of his Brother, his friend; they have confined the soul of the Mechanic in the creed and ritual of their Church; they have taken to themselves that Man of Nazareth, who never spoke of Priest or King, but with pity, reproach, or scorn.

"Brothers, be it our task to take this Son of the Carpenter, to separate his loving spirit from church and creed, and lift him, once more, before the eyes of millions, not as the Incarnation of a Church, or the Imprisoned Christ of a ferocious superstition, but as the Carpenter's Son, who first embodied the truth of Brother-

35

hood, and made it bloom in the hearts of men.

"With these three words—*The Carpenter's Son*—we can regenerate the world. We will go to the Poor. We will ask them—not to believe in the Trinity, or in the Unity of God, not in Catholic, nor in Protestant, nor in Buddha, nor in Mohammed—we will not waste time in comparing speculations, or analyzing creeds. Armed with this Christ of the Poor, we will say to the Poor, He was a Poor Man, such as you are. Like you he toiled. Like you he hungered. At the graves of Poor Men like you he wept. He lived for you—for you he died. Then listen to his voice, which utters all truth, in simple words—*Love one another.*"

The Peasant, whose animated features contrasted with the motionless lineaments of the Image by his side, now glanced around from face to face, speaking by turns to every one of his brothers. As he spoke, his voice became tremulous; his sunburnt features were wet with tears.

"And can we not accomplish the great Work for man? Is there a Brother here, who can say no! who has the heart to say it? Here we are, men of all nations, colors and creeds. Can we not join our hands around the rock, as though it were an altar, and *sacrifice our prejudices,* our creeds at the feet of the Carpenter's Son?

"Mohammedan! I speak to you. In your traditions you have read of Jesus the Prophet. Do you object to Jesus the Carpenter's Son?

"Hindoo! Your traditions speak of a mysterious incarnation—of a sublime manifestation of God enshrined in the flesh—can you refuse to acknowledge the love and Spirit of God, enshrined in the form of a Carpenter's Son?

"Protestant, it is your boast to read the written word of God. Can you refuse the Carpenter's Son?

"Catholic—your traditions speak of Church, of Authority, of Popes invested with God-like power, and men sunk beneath the degradation of the brute creation, and yet, amid this horrible mass of error, there is here and there a word—a true word of the Carpenter's Son. Are you willing to sacrifice Church Authority—Pope and Council, at the altar of Brotherhood, at the feet of the Carpenter's Son?

"Deist! It is to you I appeal. It is your delight to cherish the idea of one supreme God, only revealed to man, by the forms of external nature. Do you see God in the leaf and flower, and yet refuse to behold him in the radiant forehead, the peasant garb, the deathless words of the Carpenter's Son?

"Atheist! Yes, there is one in the band who can not believe in the existence of a God. Let me have a word with you, my brother—let us talk with each other, in kindness. You are, perchance, so constituted that the power to believe is not in your nature. All reason and no faith. And yet your heart beats warmly for the good of man; it is your earnest desire that all men may be indeed brothers. Can you find in the page of any history—in the record of any age or country—a Spirit at once so loving and so actual, so like a God and yet full of sympathy for man, as that of the Carpenter's Son? Point me to the page—produce the record—and I will love you all the better!"

His eye gleaming, his forehead radiant, the impassioned Peasant glanced around, and paused, as if to note the effect of his words. There was stillness—and then the air was full of sobs and groans.

They were not altogether sobs of anguish, groans of sorrow. They rose from their seats, they gathered round the sunburnt Peasant, and rent the air with incoherent cries.

Strange words were audible amid their cries.

"It is the Truth which our fathers sought for ages—it is the great Secret which will regenerate the World! Not the Christ of Theology, not the Catholic Christ, nor the Protestant Christ, but the Jesus of the Heart! The Carpenter's Son, separate from all Creeds, and only known as the Incarnation of Brotherhood!"

The Peasant took in his hand the veil which he had lifted from the dumb Face of the Image—his form was raised to its full stature—his eye burned as with fire from Heaven.

"Hold! Do I understand you, my brethren—are you willing to bury your creeds at the feet of the Carpenter's Son, and believe only in the Brotherhood which shines from his face? Is it so? Then let us look for the day after the long night of hopeless Evil. And I, too, am willing to offer up my creed at the feet of the Carpenter's Son!

"Listen, for I have a confession to make. I have been educated to believe that Christ was in truth the very God. That the awful Being who made the stars, and dwelt in Eternity, was present—living, throbbing—in the breast of the Nazarene. Was enshrined in the Carpenter's Son, made manifest in the flesh of that humble Son of the Poor. This I was taught to believe, and it was to me a holy thought, that Omnipotence became a suffering child of Toil, and dwelt, for a while, very humbly in the huts of the Poor, and died—feeling every pang of mortal anguish—upon a Felon's tree. Died for you—for me—for us all!

37

"And yet, my brothers, I am willing to sacrifice this belief—to consider it merely a form of words—only so that we may all meet upon one common ground, that we may all join hands around one altar, and all bind to our hearts the Spirit of the Carpenter's Son—the Incarnate form of Brotherhood among men!"

As he paused, he dropped the veil over the sad Image.

"Thus," he cried, "thus let us hide the Imprisoned Jesus of the Church. The Christ of the Heart moves in the bosom of the world. Soon the nations will know his spirit, and Kings and Priests will tremble, as the earth quivers at each throb from the Heart of the Carpenter's Son.

The Prophecy of the Peasant

"Embody the history of the Carpenter's Son, let the Spirit of his life become the Soul of our Organization, and I—a rude Peasant man, born of the humble People—can predict to you the Future of mankind!

"Not fifty years from this hour, the voice of our Brotherhood will reach the heart of a young man, in the city of Paris. Even as he sits amid a band of boon companions, the cup in his hand, and his ruddy English face contrasted with the faces of the brown Frenchmen, the voice will reach him, and he will dash the cup to the floor, and feel the impulses of his great mission stir his soul.

"His great mission? Yes—this young Englishman, encircled by the gay youth of Paris, is destined by Almighty God to conquer the New World, armed with an olive branch instead of a sword. He will cross the Ocean, he will rear a people in the wilderness, he will send forth his voice to the oppressed of all the earth, saying to them all—'Come! Here is a Home for the down-trodden, here is an Altar for the exile and the wanderer. We know neither Priest nor King, in our New World at home. We are Brothers—our Father is God!'

"And the exile and the wanderer will come, and, with this Apostle to the New World, rear the Altar of Brotherhood in the wilderness.

"Indian! The Apostle will be just to you, and to your race! Even now, as the mists which cloud the Future roll aside, I behold him standing amid the red men, near a calm river's shore—I hear the words of the Covenant which they make with each other; a Covenant made without oath, or priest, or sword, and yet it will live when oaths, and priests, and swords are known no longer upon

38

the face of the earth.

"After the Apostle has done his work, he will pass away. Years roll on—the colonists, the Emigrants, the exiles of the New World begin to grow into a People. That New World, which the Almighty has reserved for the down-trodden of all nations and races, strengthens rapidly into an Empire, such as the world has never seen before—nor of Kings, or of Priests—but an Empire of Men.

"That New World, which the Almighty has destined to be the young Heart and the young Brain of a decrepit Earth, thinking for all People, the bold thoughts of freedom; feeling for the wrongs of all races, and armed with the power to right those wrongs—the New World is assailed by all the infamies of the Old World, incarnate in the person of a King.

"He would enslave the young Empire with those customs and laws, which have drained the sap and the blood from the veins of the old, and turned an Eden into a Hell.

"But lo! The same God who sent an Apostle of Peace to plant the Olive Branch of Brotherhood on the shores of the New World, now sends a Deliverer to Assert the sanctity of the New World from all Kings, in the face of God and Man, and carve out a way for Brotherhood with his battle-sword.

"Among his legions I behold him, armed for the fight, and with the consciousness of a good Cause flashing from his eyes, and investing his bold forehead with a sublime resolve.

"The Deliverer will come in the year 1775. He will combine in his own person, all those qualities which the world has never yet seen combined in one man. He will be a man of vigorous passions, fiery-blood, temper as ardent as the southern sky. He will learn first to govern his passions, and rule his own soul, and therefore befitted for the government of men, and the sway of an Empire. Years of danger and toil in the untrodden forests, will harden him into iron manhood. He will serve, he will suffer, so that he may always feel with those who are enslaved, and know the anguish which falls to the lot of the poor man, who never ceases to suffer and endure.

"This Deliverer will rise in the darkest hour of Despotism—he will achieve the freedom of the New World, and then—

"But hold! There the cloud overcasts the future; I cannot read the future of his life after the hour when he has won the battle for Freedom.

"He may repeat the story of Cromwell, who saved his country from Kings, by usurping the power without the name.

"Yes, he may descend from his calm grandeur, as the father of his Country, and mingle in the herd of Kings, of Tyrants, of Conquerors, bartering immortal glory for the bauble of an hour.

"Then woe to America, and woe to Man!

"The New World will become the theatre of battles without an object, bloodshed without an aim. It will become a land of robbers, and of graves. The Freedom, which the Deliverer might have achieved in all its details, in the year 1783, will be postponed until 1890. A terrible postponement, a fearful delay, only marked by murder in various forms—by petty Kings, conflicting with each other under various names.

"Let it therefore be our care, my brethren, to leave to our children as a holy trust, the Life of this Deliverer! Yes, his life! A Brother of our Order will go to him, as he prepares for battle, and confront him with a Dagger and a Sword. 'This Sword is consecrated for thy defense, so long as thou art true to thy country, and to man. This Dagger is consecrated to Death, the moment thou art false!'"

"Let us write it on our records, let us teach it in our solemn ceremonies, that upon the Truth or Falsehood of this Deliverer, who will come in the year 1775, hangs the destiny of mankind, for at least three centuries.

"Does he prove true? Then the fire of Brotherhood [17] lighted by the Apostle, in the wilds of America, in 1682, and defended by the Deliverer in 1775, will illuminate the world.

"*The name of that Deliverer will become the universal word for 'Freedom.'* [18]

"Does he prove false to his great trust? Ah—that picture is too dark—it spreads before me, but I dare not contemplate its incredible details—

"In case he faithfully fulfils the awful trust confided to his hands, then behold the Future of America, and of the World!

"America, as I have said, will then in truth become the young Heart, and the young Brain of a decrepit Earth. The pulsations of the Heart, and the thoughts of that Brain, will shake the World.

"France, beautiful France—the land desecrated by religious wars and saintly massacres—will be the first to feel the throbbings of that Heart, and echo the name of the New World Deliverer amid her songs of Brotherhood.

"France will be chosen by God to fight the first battle on the soil of Europe in the cause of Man.

"The heart sickens and the eye grows dim, but to gaze upon the details of that battle, fought by France in the name of Men, against the Priests and Kings of an enslaved world.

"Even now I see it—it is there—that solitary glimpse—it is a river of blood, swelling fast into an ocean, with a corpse upon every billow. It is a people, degraded by the slavery of centuries, suddenly transformed into a horde of Demons, who not only sweep Priest and King into the bloody wave, not only level palace and jail, beneath their crimsoned feet—but—O God! can it be! they blot the name of God from the sky, and write upon the grave— 'There is no Immortality. Death is but a sleep.'

"At this period there will arise in France a Prophet of Blood. He is there—I behold him standing amid millions of slaves, drunken with their first breath of freedom. His throne, a strange engine of murder, erected on a platform, with an axe gleaming from its timbers. A slender man, with a haggard complexion, eyes filled with injected blood, features compressed, as with the impulse of an unrelenting [and ungracious and unforgiving] will, he stands upon the platform, and shouts to the freed slaves in a shrill voice, as the rich, the noble, and the beautiful, fall headless at his feet. 'More heads,' he shrieks, 'more heads for the altar of the Revolution [not Brotherhood].' More blood—more blood to wash the record of the poor man's wrongs from the history of ages! The rich have had the world long enough—it is now the day of the poor.' [19]

"It will be a terrible day for Kings, and for the rich men, who believe in Kings, when this Messiah of Carnage comes up from the cloud of Revolution; a lurid Meteor, shining with a pale, gloomy grandeur over a world of blood!

"He will arise in France, I say, he will arise after the Deliverer of the New World hath done his work, and he will prepare the way for the coming of a Crowned Avenger.

"And even he will feel the divine beauty of the Carpenter's Son, and hope for a calm time of Brotherhood, after the tempest of infernal passion is over.

"At last he will fall beneath the gory wheels of Revolution— beneath those wheels, which were hurled onward by his own arm— but in the moment of his fall, he will foresee the coming of the blessed day of Brotherhood.

"Nay—he will die upon the unknown engine of murder, which was his throne [the Reaction of the Law], by the very axe which has drunk the blood of royalty and beauty—he will die a wretched and accursed thing [hated and accursed because *so* he thought and acted], his last groan chorused by the demon yells of that Mob, who

41

were yesterday his Brethren—but in his last moment, a Hope will brighten over his glassy eyes, and his clotted lips will tremble with the accents of Prophecy—

" 'After me a Crowned Avenger comes! When my body is in the ditch, and my name given out to all the world as a Proverb of loathing, the Crowned Avenger will start from the People—he will write his name upon the Globe in characters of Fire. He will avenge me![20]

" 'Without me, this Crowned Avenger could never have appeared. I have prepared the way for him—I go to darkness, and no one pities me. And he, too, will be crushed beneath the weight of his greatness, he, too, will prepare the way for another, and a Nobler man.

" 'And when the day of that Nobler man, that Universal Liberator, comes—when nations and empires, and dynasties, and sects and creeds, have crumbled into dust before the light of Brotherhood, and the freed earth shall glow with gladness under the eyes of God—then shall justice be done to my memory, and men shall no longer couple my name with curses, but speak of me as one who sacrificed, not merely life, but fame, for the sake of the Poor.' "

The Supreme Chief of the Rosy Cross

"And this"—faltered the speaker, wiping the moisture from his brow—"this will occur before the Eighteenth Century is done—yes—I behold even now a terrible date, written in black characters upon a lurid cloud—the date is 1789!

"Yes, Priests and Kings will drink to the last dregs the cup which they filled for the lips of their slaves. They will have to combat, not merely a horde of Slaves, but a Mob of Demons.

"But in order that the freedom, so fearfully won by the People transformed into Demons, may not be lost in endless massacre, a Man will arise, who will place his foot upon the necks of Kings and mock their power to scorn by assuming a power, unknown before in the annals of the human race. That boundless power will be assumed and worn in the name of the People.

"The New World demanded first an Apostle, then a Deliverer. Europe demands a crowned peasant—an *Avenger*.

"Rising from the common herd, this man will become the Cromwell of a World, believing not so much in the people as in armies; not so much in God as in his own Destiny.

"His bold forehead, stamped with more than kingly grandeur,

his eyes lighted by a soul conscious of its own Destiny, his features shadowed into the warm bronze of the south, and marked by the outlines of the oriental races, appear before me now, like the face of a Demi-God.

"He traverses Europe, leaving his bloody footprints upon every shore. He stands upon the Egyptian pyramid, and, with his sad, thoughtful eyes, surveys a world that is to be conquered by him. He girdles one-half the world with a belt of cannon and musquet, bayonet and sword. Not a land in the Old World but is peopled by his armies—already he stretches forth his arm toward the New.

"And this man—the Crowned Avenger of the People—with all his blood-shed, is a holy thing in the eyes of Heaven, compared with the noblest King on the face of the earth.

"He comes to begin for Europe that work which the Apostle and the Deliverer accomplished for the New World.

"And after his work is done, and he has scourged the Kings as with the lash of a God, and made them the humble ministers of his will, he will be delivered into their hands; and, afraid of the Man, even when they have possession of his body, the Kings will bury the Crowned Peasant in the profound solitudes of an Island that stands alone in the centre of an ocean.

"There, isolated from mankind, and secluded with his own heart, the Avenger will die, his last gasp embittered by the persecutions of petty men, with brows of clay and hearts of stone.

"After the body is dead, and Kings have worked their will upon it, the Soul of the Avenger will come back to France, and throb with terrible life in new revolutions.

"That soul, redeemed from the stains which darkened its beauty, will hover, like a good omen, over the destiny of mankind, and dwell in the hearts of the French people, as the thunder dwells in the clouds of heaven.

"For the soul prepared the way for the coming of a Deliverer for Europe, even as the thunder and the lightning precede the glorious calm of the summer day.

"And he will come—yes, the Deliverer of Europe—of the world, perchance—he will come at last.* There are various figures writ-

---

* In the Archives of the Supreme Council of the Brotherhood, which has remained unknown to the world and even multitudes of its members, there is a legend that in the New Age—in which we now live—one of lowly birth, free from malice, hatred and revenge, but whose heart is unselfish and filled with Brotherhood, will come and teach the Law, that the Law will be accepted by the individuals, who, governing themselves thereby, will establish Brotherhood among men without the shedding of blood or the sowing of hatred and dissention.

ten on the clouds of the Future, and I may not read them now.

"There—glorious date, that tells of a world enfranchised by the spirit of Brotherhood embodied in the Carpenter's Son—it tosses before me, amid clouds of rainbow beauty. Is it 1848—or is it 1884?—there is a mist before my eyes—I cannot trace the figures plainly, but

"—The Deliverer of Europe—of the world—will come at last, and come with the arm to avenge and the *spirit to love!*

"Kings will shrink from their thrones at his coming; the slaves of the Old World will start into a people, and even the black slaves of the New World will dare to claim a portion for themselves in the Love of God, and grasp for themselves a share in the Brotherhood of Man.

"Even the red man of the forest, smitten by the iron finger of White Civilization, which poisoned his heart and withers his brain, will look up and see the face of the Carpenter's Son, smiling blessings upon him even from the ruins of Despotism and Superstition.

"Thus, my brothers, you have before you the three great Epochs which will mark the history of Man, within the next three hundred years.

"First, the Epoch of the Apostles, who, armed with the Love which dwelt in the breast of the Carpenter's Son, will rear the altar of Brotherhood on the shores of the New World, thus promulgating to all mankind the Divine Truth, that the New World is not for Priests or Kings, nor for any form of *superstition or privilege,* but for Man—sacred and set apart by God for the millions who toil.[21]

"Second, the Epoch of the Deliverer, who, called by God, will take up the sword, and even as the Carpenter's Son scourged the money-changers from the Temple of Jerusalem, so will he scourge the oppressors of body and soul from that Holiest Temple of Brotherhood, the land of the New World.

"In case the Deliverer, after giving freedom to the New World, proves false to his trust,[22] and takes to himself a Crown and Throne, then the history of the Future is beset by clouds that have no ray to lighten their omnipotent gloom.

"But should he prove faithful to his great trust, and after accomplishing the work of freedom, yield his sword into the hands of the people, and become, for the sake of the Holy Cause, a Man among Men, a Brother among Brothers, then will follow—

"The Third Epoch. The Epoch of the Crowned Avenger, whose tremendous battles, supernatural glory, and Death sublime

44

in its very isolation, will prepare the world for the approach of the Holiest Epoch, for the Coming of the Universal Liberator.[23]

"The Epoch of Brotherhood among men—the Liberator of all classes, nations, and races of the great family.

"In the year of the Carpenter's Son 1848, or in 1884,* this Epoch and this Liberator will be announced by convulsions all over the world.

"Monarchy, grown drunk with its habit of oppression and bloodshed, will press the millions who toil, to the last extent of sufferance and endurance. Rich Men will say, triumphantly, that there is no God but Gold, no Heaven but in getting more wealth, no hell but in Poverty. They will regard the Poor—that is, nine-tenths of the human family, as old fables tell us, the Damned are regarded by the Fiends—as the object of alternate mockery and vengeance; as things of dumb wood and stone; as beasts; as anything but souls born of God and redeemed by his Spirit, incarnate in the Son of the Carpenter.

"Rich Men will gather round the Throne in England, and urge Monarchy—already bloated with crime—to new exactions, and place in its grasp incredible improvements in the kingly art of murder.

"Rich Men in Ireland will pour into the cup of that People's woe—that cup which has been slowly filling for centuries—the last drop of bitterness. The cup of Ireland's despair will be full at last, and the Rich Man will have to drink it from the hand of a Demon, who was once a peasant, once a man.

"Rich Men in America will strengthen the chains by which millions of the Black race are held in bondage. They will regard these millions of the Black race as beasts of the field, and herd them together in profitable Incest; selling the fruit of the mother's womb before it has seen the light, and holding Property in Human Flesh, in Human Blood, in Immortal Souls." [24]

A groan echoed from the assemblage.

"This in America? This in the New World?

"Yes! This in the land for which the Deliverer has consecrated his sword! In order that Man may know the value of freedom, it is *necessary that he should first suffer the pains of hell, in the ditch of slavery.* And, of all the forms of slavery which the world ever saw, or ever will see, that which will curse the American Continent, in the year 1848, or 1884—under the name of Black Slavery, stands

---

* The beginning of the New Dispensation. The operation of the Law of this New Era will be gradually as will be the elimination of the Unjust.

arrayed before my vision as the most appalling. It is—pardon the warmth of my utterance, for over the mists of the future I see, even now, in its garb of crimes—it is an Infernal Trinity, composed of three Fiends, who are called Atheism, Incest, Blasphemy.

"Atheism, but not honest Atheism which denies a God in Nature, and blunders upon a something called chance; but a ferocious Atheism, which builds altars to God, worships him with the pomp of priest and ritual, and at the same moment shows that it does not believe in his existence, does not fear his vengeance, for it degrades his Image into a brute.

"Incest, for in order to make Flesh and Blood more profitable, it encourages . . .

"Blasphemy, for it not only makes the New World a reproach on the lips of the Tyrant of the old world, but it turns all that is holy in religion into a Lie. It cries, "Hail, Lord Jesus!" and with that cry, treads the Black Brother of the Carpenter's Son into deeper bondage.

"When the blessed Epoch is very near—when the footsteps of the Universal Liberator begins to move the earth—in fact, the Slaves over all the world—will rise upon their masters, rise without an object or an aim, but urged to ferocious action, by an impulse which cannot be resisted or controlled.

"Then will occur the Jubilee of brute force, the Saturnalia of Murder. It will be a day of reckoning for the Rich Man over all the World. He will learn at last, that it is better to give some light of education, some gleam of immortality, even to a slave. He will, I say, learn that it is better to combat an educated slave, whose nature retains some ray of its Divine origin, much better, as God lives! than to combat a Brute in human shape, who knows no limit in his vengeance, and sacrifices, in his hellish fury, not only the rich man, but the beautiful wife who nestles in his arms and the little child who clings to his knees.

"It will be a terrible going out of Egypt—an Exodus of incredible carnage, which the Poor will accomplish, ere the great day of their redemption.

"The Israelites of old, chained in Egypt, went forth one day, and the sea, parting on either side, left bare a safe pathway for the liberated slaves. Their pursuers followed, and were lost in the waves. The freed slaves beheld their livid faces, and heard their impotent cries of despair. This was indeed a terrible sight for Egypt, but a glorious day for Israel.

"Remember, however, that the Israelites, enslaved by the

Egyptians, only symbolized the Poor Man all over the world, en-slaved by the Rich.

"Therefore, I say, it will be a terrible going out of Egypt which the Poor Man will accomplish, when all at once he escapes from thraldom, through a Red Sea. That Red Sea nothing but the blood which flows from the veins of the tyrants of the Poor.

"It will, I repeat, be an Exodus of incredible carnage, which the Angels will behold on that day, when the Poor Man shall hear the voice of God, calling upon him in his bondage—'Arise!' The hour has come. The cup is full. Arise, ye millions of the human race— Arise, ye races and tribes of the Poor! Go out from the bondage, though the way of your redemption is paved with the bodies of the Rich, though their blood rolls before you like a sea. Go out from bondage! For it is the Exodus of the Poor, for which we have waited and endured, and wept your bloody tears so long!'

"And the same God who gave Moses to the chained Israelites, will call forth, from the shadows in the year 1848, or 1884—the Liberator of a world."

The man with sunburnt features and knotted hands, stood alone, near the veiled figure, the centre of a group, agitated by emotion too deep for words.

They looked upon him, as he arose in their midst, clad like an humble peasant, and felt that he was a Prophet—despite his toil-hardened hands and coarse attire—a Prophet called from the ranks of the Poor, to foretell the future of a World in chains.

Overwhelmed by the intensity of his thoughts, the Peasant rested both hands upon the shoulder of the veiled figure, while his chest shook as with intense physical torture, and the cold damps stood in beads upon his brow. His eyes grew brighter every moment, while the brown hue of his bold countenance was marked by a death-like pallor.

"At last," he murmured amid the writhings of his inexplicable agony. "At last, Blessed Lord, the Lead [the dead letter of religion] will become Gold [spiritualized and vital], and the Sneer be changed into a Smile."

It was a long time, ere the sensation created by the words of this rude Prophet, permitted the members of this secret Brotherhood to give utterance to their thoughts in speech.

The aged Swede arose.

His white hairs waved in the wind, which came in fitful gusts from the mouth of the cavern, and the faint light imparted its gloomy radiance to his withered features.

47

In a tremulous voice, he spoke of the great object which had called the Chiefs of the Rosy Cross from all quarters of the globe— [to the cavern in far Germany].

They had been called, not so much by the command of a Supreme Chief, as by the voice of a tradition, which had been treasured in the innumerable branches,[25] or Circles of the great Brotherhood, since the earlier years of the Tenth Century.[26]

That tradition pointed out a particular year in the seventeenth century, which would witness a New Era in the History of the Order.

On the appointed year, at a certain hour of a certain day, the Chiefs of the Brotherhood, from all quarters of the globe, were to assemble—the tradition enjoined—in the cavern of a German mountain, long known in the history of the Order.

They were to choose by lot a Supreme Chief, who would be known all over the world, to all the Brothers of the Rosy Cross, and to all secret orders, beneath the Brotherhood,[26] by a certain symbol, engraved on a golden medal.

The Symbol was a Globe, a Rising Sun, and a Cross, encircled by the Hebrew words, in the Hebrew character—

VAYOMER ELOHEIM YEHEE AUR VAYEHEE AUR.*

"These words," continued the aged Swede, **"indicate the Light which, shining from the councils of our Brotherhood, shall illuminate all the world. A light spoken into existence by the voice of God, which shall do the work of God in every human heart.** Brothers, to me, as the oldest of the Chiefs, has this medal been entrusted. It was given into my hands, by a Chief who had reached the venerable age of one hundred years. I now surrender it into your hands—I place it upon this rock, which forms the altar of our worship. Let no one touch it, nor gaze upon it, until the Supreme Chief of the Brotherhood is elected."

He placed the Medal on the altar, where it glimmered with a pale golden light.

An inexplicable sensation pervaded the assemblage, as every eye was centred upon this most sacred symbol of the Order. It was endeared to their hearts by a thousand ceremonies; it was linked with the overwhelming associations of the ancient renown and almost Godlike power of the Brotherhood, in the days of old.

The Hebrew words rudely graved upon it, gave some color to the tradition which taught that it had been coined by the hand of

---

* According to Hebrew scholars this should be *vayomer Elohim Yehi OR Vayehi OR.*

the High Priest Aaron, in the days of the Wilderness.

True, the globe and the cross seemed to indicate a much more recent origin. Yet the globe was known as an emblem in the secret Brotherhood, long before it was discovered that the earth itself was a globe. The Cross is found in the pyramids of Egypt, erected thousands of years before the era of the Carpenter's Son.

In a word, this medal, glimmering dimly upon the surface of the rock, overwhelmed the Brothers with the memories of three thousand years.

Now commenced the ceremonial of election.

Every chief wrote his name upon a tablet. Their tablets were given into the hands of the Swede, who placed them in a hollow of the rock, which supplied the place of an Urn.

"One by one, you will advance, my Brothers, and draw a single tablet from the hollow in the rock. It is asserted by the traditions of our Order, that the great work of the Supreme Chief will fall upon the Brother who draws the tablet on which the sign of the Cross is traced. Advance, my Brothers—but hold—let me first ask every Brother to raise his clasped hands above his head, and swear by the Globe, by the Rising Sun and the Cross, to be faithful to the Supreme Chief, whom we are about to elect from our midst— to obey his commands without hesitation, scruple or reserve, and to recognize his Power, whenever it is attested by the most sacred symbol of our Order!" [27]

There was a pause—and then from every lip arose the solemn chorus: "We swear by the Globe, by the Rising Sun, and by the Cross!" Perchance the outward history of the world, that history which only pictures the appearances, not the realities of things, never described a scene of sterner grandeur, than that which was now in progress within the walls of the mountain cavern.

The Representatives of the various Destinies of Nations, were met in awful Council, to decide the Destiny of all mankind, to elect, in fact, one man, who should in his turn embody the destiny of a World.

One by one they came toward the hollow in the rock. The torch-light shone upon their various costumes, and displayed the workings of those contrasted faces, every one the representative of a People, the type of a race. The blanket of the Indian, adorned with the many-colored wampum-belt, contrasted with the turban and flowing robes of the Moslem, the tawny Hindoo, the bronzed Spaniard, the florid German, mingled together in that throng; and the hardy Colonist from New England stood side by side with the stern soldier of Cromwell, and the down-trodden Son of Ireland.

The Jesuit, too, folding his hands over his black robe, with a deep thought upon his tonsured brow, stood near the worshipper of Con-fav-tse from the far land of China.

The Black Man was not alone. His jet-black features, scarred with the traces of that incredible thraldom from which he was a fugitive, he joined hands with the agile Son of Italy, whose sculptured lineaments spoke of the races of Ancient Rome.

The gray-garbed Peasant stood alone, leaning upon the veiled figure with his knotted hands. Few could guess his country or his race. His bold features, darkened by the sun, spoke somewhat of an Oriental race. The rumor ran from lip to lip, that he was from an island in the Mediterranean.

His thoughts were absorbed by the overwhelming solemnity of the moment.

They were about to elect a Man, who would control for good or evil—for good or evil in the present age, and through all future time—the immense organization of the Brotherhood.

On whom would the great work fall?

The Turk, the Hindoo, the Arab—the eyes of the Peasant roved along the throng—or perchance—the Black Man? By the chance or fatality of that mysterious lottery, the destiny of the Order and the World might be embodied in a Negro—a Negro! One of that thrice degraded race, who have been ever doomed to drain the bitterest dregs of slavery, and wear its heaviest chain upon their lacerated souls.

Meanwhile the aged Swede sat apart; his white beard floating over his breast. His days were numbered; he was not a Candidate for the great office, and more than this, he had been the last keeper of the Sacred Symbol of Brotherhood. He was therefore not a Candidate, but a Judge.

While the Peasant stood leaning against the veiled figure, the other brethren advanced one by one to the hollow in the rock, and turning their faces away, drew forth a single tablet from the darkness.

The Peasant was aroused from his reverie by the voice of the Swede—

"Brother, it is now your turn," he said.

The Peasant looked around with a stare of vague amazement.

"Have all drawn but me?" he exclaimed.

Even as he spoke, he beheld the brethren standing against the walls of the cavern, with their tablets in their hands.

50

"Is not the tablet with the Cross yet drawn?" he ejaculated, while a tremor seized his limbs—"and have all the Brothers advanced to the rock—all but me?"

"No," answered the Swede—"There are three others besides you—"

The Peasant followed the extended hand of the Swede, and beheld standing near him, the Indian, the Colonist from New England, and the Black Man.

"On one of the four will fall the office of Supreme Chief!" exclaimed the Swede.

Then it was that a wild suspense seized every breast, and all eyes were turned upon the four. The Indian and the Black Man stood on the right of the veiled figure—the New England Colonist on the left. The Peasant, leaning upon the leaden image, trembled from head to foot, and veiled his face.

"Advance, Brother from the New World," he cried in a husky voice—"The tablet marked with the Cross is yours!"

The Colonist advanced with a firm step, but his hand trembled, his face changed color, as he drew a single tablet from the hollow in the rock. He dared not look upon it, but stood gazing with a vacant glance in the face of the Swede.

"Is it the tablet marked with the Cross?" interrogated the Peasant, as he raised his face—his voice, changed and hollow, resembled a prolonged groan.

The interest of the Chiefs became intense and painful.

"The tablet! The tablet!" was heard in murmurs—and in various tongues on every side.

The Colonist at last gathered courage; he gazed upon the tablet—

"My own name!" he said, and turned away.

The stillness which succeeded, was like the grave.

The contest was now between the Peasant, the Indian, and the Black Man. The Indian next advanced. Stern and proudly erect, he wound his blanket over his broad chest, and his aquiline profile was described in the bold shadow on the wall of the cavern, as he drew near the hollow in the rock.

Extending his hand without a tremor, he also drew forth a solitary tablet, and held it toward the light.

You could not hear the faintest echo of a sound. All was terribly still.

"The name of my Hindoo Brother," said the Indian, as he resumed his place.

51

The office of Supreme Chief now lay between the Peasant and the Black Man.

As for the Peasant, seized by an uncontrollable emotion, he bowed his tall form once more against the Leaden Image, and concealed his face from the light.

The Black Man advanced a step—hesitated—and returned to his place.

"Brother, it is your time," and as he spoke, he turned his harsh features toward the Peasant.

There was no reply. The Peasant, who but a moment ago had seemed a Prophet, inspired for a great work, now rested his arms upon the Leaden Image and hid his face, while his strong frame shook with agony.

"Advance, brother," exclaimed the Swede to the Negro. "The Office of Supreme Chief is within your grasp!"

The Peasant heard the words of the Swede, and a cold shudder pervaded his limbs. So near, so very near that Power, which held in its hand the Destiny of the human race, and yet it was about to glide from his touch. He heard the footsteps of the Black Man—he knew by the dead stillness that the Negro was standing near the hollow in the rock—he felt as he heard the universal ejaculation that the Negro had become the Supreme Chief of the Order.

Yet hark! The voice of the Black Man is heard—

"I have drawn a tablet, on which my Red Brother's name is written," he said, and all was still again.

The heart of the Peasant bounded within his breast. Possessed in every nerve by an intense ambition, he had writhed with all the agony of suspense, and now his blood became fire, with the pulsation of a boundless joy.

The tablet on which the Cross was traced was his own—with his form bowed and his face concealed, he awaited the salutations of his brethren. But suddenly his blood grew cold again, as the voice of the Swede fell on his ear:

"Brother, advance. You are the last. Two tablets alone remain in the hollow of the rock. On one your name is written, for it has not been drawn by any of the brethren. On the other the Cross is traced. *In case you do not draw the Tablet with the Cross, a new election will be held.*"

The Peasant heard the last words, and raised his head. Every eye remarked the pallor of his face.

"Two tablets!" he echoed, with a vacant stare—"I had forgotten—" he paused, and turning his eyes upon the throng, he exclaimed—"I am not worthy of the awful trust, I will not place my hand in the hollow of the rock. Let the tablets be cast into that hollow once more, and the great office will doubtless fall to the lot of some more worthy brother."

But they silenced him with their murmurs—every one, from the Swede to the Black Man, bade him advance.

It was a terrible moment for that rude Peasant, with the gray garb and sunburnt face, when, crossing the cavern floor, shading his agitated features from the light, he placed his knotted hand in the hollow of the rock. He felt the two tablets beneath his fingers. He knew not which to take. One moment he desired the great office with all his soul, the next, he felt unworthy, and hoped that he might draw the tablet inscribed with his own name.

"It is an awful Power to be placed in the hands of one man," he muttered, as he raised his hand, and without daring to gaze upon the tablet, held it behind his back toward the light.

The Swede arose.

"You suffer, my brother," he whispered—"your face is like the face of a dead man—I will read the tablet for you."

The Peasant could not speak a word, but he listened to the footsteps of the Swede. There was a moment's pause—he could feel the intense interest of the Brotherhood, as he heard the sound of their deep-drawn breath.

"Brothers, behold!"—it was the voice of the Swede, and the Peasant, with his face turned from the light, heard the cry which filled the cavern. That cry echoed from the very hearts of the assembled brethren, as every eye beheld the tablet which the old man held toward the light.

And yet the Peasant dared not turn and know his destiny. That murmur was so confused, so vague, he could not divine the true meaning, but he felt the hand of the Swede upon his own, and felt himself urged gently to the light.

"Brothers! salute the Supreme Chief of our Brotherhood!" the voice of the Swede swelled through the cavern.

For a moment the Peasant tottered to and fro, while his sight grew dim, and the figures of the brethren flitted before him like the confused shapes of a dream. But that moment over, his sight grew clear, his limbs were firm—glancing around with unwavering eyes, he beheld himself encircled by the Chiefs of the Brotherhood, he felt the Golden Medal in his hand.

"Now—" he said, while a deep rapture softened his bold features, and his form, clad in humble peasant attire, towered in the centre of that throng—"Now, indeed, my work is before me. It is for me to embody in the ritual of our Brotherhood, the life of the Carpenter's Son!"

Joining hands, they encircled him, and pronounced with one accord, in the unknown tongue, the ancient formula of the Order. The Swede laid his withered hand upon his brown hairs and blessed him—Hindoo, Turk, Jesuit, Indian, Englishman and Spaniard, Dane and German, gathered around, a rampart of living hearts.

The Negro, as the most degraded and down-trodden of all earth's children, pronounced the last word of the consecration—

"It is from a Child of Toil that the Children of Toil must look for their redemption."

The Supreme Chief of the Brotherhood raised the Golden Medal toward the light, and examined its details with a careful scrutiny.

"On one side the Globe, the Cross and the Rising Sun, with the inscription, 'VAYOMER ELOHEIM YEHEE AUR, VAYEHEE AUR' —'Then spoke God, Let there be light, and there was light.' The reverse of the Medal is blank. It bears no inscription. One day it will have an inscription, a glorious inscription, but not until earth is redeemed and all men are Brothers!

"Yes, long ages after we are dead, my brethren, some Chief of our Order will write upon the blank side of the Medal—

"*Earth redeemed by the Spirit of the Carpenter's Son, embodied in the Brotherhood of the Rosy Cross.*'"

The speaker took a sharp-pointed dagger from his breast, and resting the medal upon the rock, traced in rude characters, two dates, beneath the symbol of the Order. These dates were "1777" and "1848-84." [28]

Then turning to the silent Brotherhood, he exclaimed—

"In the year 1777, another general convocation of the Chiefs of the Brotherhood will be held in the land of the New World. Then the Golden Medal will again be placed in the hands of a Supreme Chief, elected in accordance with the injunction of the most aged Chief. Until that time—in case I die before it arrives—the office of Supreme Chief will remain vacant. And in the year 1848—or 84, a general convocation will be held, at a point to be designated by the Supreme Chief elected in the year 1777."

Glancing into the faces of the encircling Chiefs, the Peasant, now become the Supreme Power of the Order, beckoned with his hand to seven brethren, who separated themselves from the throng, and took their places at his side.

"These are the Supreme Elders of the Brotherhood, appointed

by me to assist in the government of the Order, and to receive the sacred symbol in case of my death. They are known in our traditions as THE SEVEN. Brother," he continued, turning to the first of the Seven—" "Your name and country?"

The First of the Seven was a man of commanding presence, with a face traced with the indications of a serene soul.

"I was born in England," he said, "but now that my native land is a home no longer for freemen, I have no country. I am about to depart to the New World. Not to New England, for it is accursed by the Demon of Persecution, but to a more southern clime. My name is Lawrence Washington."

The Peasant wrote that name upon the Tablet *marked with the Cross.* "Washington!" he murmured, as though he had heard of it before.

The Supreme Chief turned to the Second of the Seven. A man of slender frame, sharp features, stamped with an iron resolution, and eyes full of enthusiasm.

"Your country, Brother, and your name?"

"I am of France," responded a shrill, discordant voice. "My name is Robespierre."

The Supreme Chief shuddered as he wrote that name underneath the first.

"I have seen it," he murmured, in a tone inaudible to the Brethren—"I have seen it in my dreams, written in red characters, upon the timbers of that unknown engine of Murder."

To the third he turned. The harsh features of the Black Man met his gaze.

"I have no name," cried the Negro. "I am called Isaac the Slave."

After he had written the designation of the African beneath the other names he turned to the Fourth. The Indian, standing alone, with his blanket falling over his broad chest.

"My country? Wherever the White Race leaves our people a wigwam or a hunting ground. Write, Supreme Chief, that my name is Talondoga, and my country the Land of the Setting Sun."

"Thy children," murmured the Peasant, "shall yet sweep the white race with fire and sword."

The Fifth answered proudly—"I am a German. A tiller of the soil. Write, John the Serf; and as for country, say that I have no Fatherland but the grave."

It was now the turn of the Sixth. A dark-visaged Hindoo, clad in the garb of the lowest order of Hindoo Priesthood.

55

"Buldarh of the far Eastern land—a Pariah, who has no lower *caste* beneath him."

"Thy country shall be given up awhile to Moloch, incarnate in the English Monarchy. But when the oppressor has trampled you for a hundred years, you will learn his cunning, and crush him with his own weapons."

Thus speaking, this Peasant Ruler wrote the name of the Pariah beneath that of the German Serf.

The Seventh: an Italian, whose face seemed oppressed with the Doom of his country.

"Giovanni Ferreti!" murmured the Supreme Chief, as he wrote this name beneath the others. "Fear not, Italian! Humble artisan as you are, it is from your race that there will spring a high-souled Man, who will strike astonishment into the hearts of all men, for he will embody in his own person, the function of Pope and Liberator!"

"There are the names of your Elders—of the Seven," exclaimed the Supreme, after a pause—"Let us behold them, and write them in our hearts—"

And he held the tablet before the eyes of the Brethren. These names were written underneath the Cross:

1. Lawrence Washington.
2. Robespierre.
3. Isaac the Slave.
4. Talondoga the Indian.
5. The German Serf.
6. Buldarh the Hindoo and Pariah.
7. Giovanni Ferreti.

"It only remains for me to write my own name," said the Supreme Chief, with a sad smile. These words excited a universal interest. Every Brother was anxious to know the name of this man, who had been called by Destiny to the supreme sway of the Brotherhood.

"My father," he said, "was an Arab, who, cast ashore upon an Island in the Mediterranean, was enslaved by a Lord, whose castle is built among the rocks. My mother was a native of the island. As I do not know the name of my father in the Arab tongue, I will—after the manner óf slaves over all the world—take the name of the lord who enslaved my father. The race of that Lord has become extinct; himself, his children, all his people, were swept away by plague; but the Son of the Arab Slave will perpetuate their name—"

And beneath the names of the Seven, he wrote the words—

"LEON BUONAPARTE OF CORSICA." *

His bronzed features grew radiant, his dark eyes gathered new light, as he gazed upon that name.

"Perchance, at some future day," he said, "that name of the extinct Italian noble, who built his castle on the rocks of Corsica— that name, now assumed by his Slave, may shake the world, and read, to the eyes of Kings, like the handwriting on Belshazzar's wall!"

And raising his right hand, which grasped the Golden Medal, toward heaven, he stood motionless as stone, while his eyes, shining with prophetic light, seemed to behold already a world of slaves starting from their chains, and building, upon the wrecks of Despotism and Superstition, the sublime altar of human Brotherhood.

"The Day is breaking, my brothers, and we must separate," he said, as he took the torch and drew near the veiled figure once more. "But before you hasten to your stations, in the various regions of the globe, we will meet again. Then—at our next meeting, which shall not be many days from the present hour—I will reveal to you the regenerated ceremonial of our Brotherhood. Yes, I will reveal to you the new organization of the Order, in which the Spirit of the Carpenter's Son shall throb and burn as the life of all life. Armed with this spirit—embodied in ritual and constitution—you will hasten to your various circles, scattered over the surface of the Globe, and swell your divisions of the great Fraternity, by new converts, and go on in your great work, until the masses begin to feel that the Spirit of the Carpenter's Son, freed from the body of the leaden [dead, formulastic, creed-bound] Church, walks divinely over the earth again, speaking to the poor, words that are mightier than armies.

"Yes—I anticipate the question which rises to your lips and shines in your eyes. You ask me, what manner of scene from the life of the Carpenter's Son, I would embody in the ritual of the Order? The question is not difficult to answer.

"Have you ever heard of the day, when that Carpenter's Son arose in a Nazarene Synagogue, and proclaimed, clad, as he was, in the gaberdine of toil, proclaimed in the face of the Rich Man and the Priest, that the Spirit of God was upon him to preach good tidings to the Poor, liberty to the bondman, the good time of

---

* Shortly after this meeting, the French Lafayette, friend of New America, became a member of the Great Council as representative to America.

57

Brotherhood to all men?

"Or, have you ever heard of the Rich Man, who came one day to the Carpenter's Son, and, won by the divine beauty of that Spirit which shone in his eyes, asked sorrowfully, "Master, what shall I do to inherit eternal life?"

"The Carpenter's Son looked in the face of the Rich Man, marked his robes of fine linen and purple, and then said, in that voice which melted the souls of all who listened to its music—

" 'Sell all thou hast and give to the Poor!'"

"Such scenes as these we will embody in our ritual, and make the life of our life! Yes, to the Poor we will preach good tidings, liberty, light! But to the Rich, armed with the Justice of the Carpenter's Son, we will thunder the sentence which God has pronounced upon their heads—'Sell all thou hast and give to the Poor! Restore to the mass of mankind the lands which ye have *stolen* from them, and Baptized with their blood! Divide among the Poor your *ill-gotten* gold—give back, give back, in the name of God, your *Usurped power*, and let your tardy Repentance be aided by a strict and universal Restitution!'"

The words had not passed his lips, when he dashed the torch upon the ground, and the cavern was enveloped in darkness. By the last rays, the Brothers beheld his sunburnt features flashing as with a divine radiance, and through the darkness, they heard him speak in a low, deep voice, tremulous with unutterable joy—

"Then, indeed, shall the Lead become Gold, and the Sneer be changed into a Smile."

The Law of the Present Dispensation

They who labor not shall neither reap nor shall unto them be given. None but the sower shall reap the grain and garner the harvest.

"Render unto Caesar that which belongs to Caesar and unto
God that which belongs to God,"
BUT
"Thou shalt not steal" nor shalt thou "Covet that
which belongs to thy neighbor."
AND
"By the sweat of thy brow shalt thou live,"
BUT
"The Laborer is worthy of his hire."

THE FULFILMENT OF THE PROPHECY
THE CONSECRATION OF WASHINGTON
The Deliverer
THE WISSAHIKON

Wissahikon! *

That name, soft as the wind of May, breathing its perfume over
the brow of the way-worn wanderer—melodious as a burst of
music, swelling from afar, over the bosom of still waters—sad and
wild, as the last groan of a dying warrior, who, conquering all vain
regrets by one strong impulse of his passing soul, sternly gives up
his life to God—*Wissahikon!*

That name speaks to our hearts with a pathos all its own. Yes,
it speaks to our hearts with a strange and mingled meaning,
whether written Wissahickon, or Wissahiccon, or pronounced as
it fell from the lips of the Indian maidens in the olden time, who
bathed their forms in its waters, and adorned their raven hair with
the lilies and wild roses that grow in its deep woods—*Wissahikone!*

That word speaks of rocks, piled up in colossal grandeur, with
waves murmuring at their feet, and dark green pines blooming forever on their brows.

That name tells me of a tranquil stream, that flows from the
fertile meadows of Whitemarsh, and then cleaves its way for eight
miles, through rocks of eternal granite, now reflecting on its waves
the dark grey walls and steep roof of some forest hidden mill, now
burying itself beneath the *shadows* of overhanging trees, and then
comes laughing into the sun, like a maiden smiling at the danger
that is past.

We will go down to Wissahikon.

---

* *Wissahikon* is much *more* than a word, or the name of a stream, however beautiful. To the *true* American it is synonymous with a pure Mystic religion, with the
freedom of ·all religious sects, for it was here that the many sectarians established
themselves; with the founding of the American Republic, because here was conceived
the Constitution, and here was held the first American Rosicrucian Supreme Council,
here was Washington, one of its Acolytes Consecrated, and here was formed the Grand
Temple of the Rosy Cross. Wissahikon the beautiful and, to many of us, Sacred as
the Ganges is to the Hindoo.

59

You have been there; some of you in the still summer afternoon, when the light laugh of girlhood rang through the woods—some of you perchance in the early dawn, or in the purple twilight when the shadows came darkly over the waters.

But to go down into its glens at midnight, when silence like death is brooding there! Then the storm-cloud gathers like a pall— then, clinging to yon awful cliff that yawns above the blackness, you hear the Thunder speak to the still woods, and the deeps far below, speak back again their Thunder. Then at dead of night, you see the red lightning flashing down over the tall pines, down over the dark waters, quivering and trembling with its arrows of wrath, far into the shadows of the glen.

At last the storm-cloud rolls back its pall. The silver moon comes shining out, smiling from her window in the sky. The Eagle, too, lord of the wild domain, starts from his perch, and wheels through the deep azure circling round them, bathing his pinions in her light as he looks for the coming of his God, the sun.

Had you been there at dead of night, as I have been, you would know something of the supernatural grandeur, the awful beauty of the Wissahikon; even though you were an Atheist, you would have knelt down and felt the existence of a God.

The Wissahikon wears a beauty all its own. True, the Hudson is magnificent with her mingled panorama of mountain and valley, tumultuous river and tranquil bay. To me she seems a Queen, who reposes in strange majesty, a crown of snow upon her forehead of granite, the leaf of the Indian corn, the spear of wheat, mingled in the girdle which binds her waist, the murmur of rippling water ascending from the valley beneath her feet.

The Susquehanna is awfully sublime; a warrior who rushes from his home in the forest, hews his way through primeval mountains, and howls in his wrath as he hurries to the ocean. Ever and anon, like a Conqueror overladened with the spoils of battle, he scatters a green island in his path, or like the same Conqueror relenting from the fury of the fight, smiles like Heaven in the wavelets of some tranquil bay.

Neither Queen, nor warrior is the Wissahikon.

Let us look at its Image, as it rises before us.

A Prophetess, who with her cheek embrowed by the sun, and her dark hair—not gathered in clusters or curling in ringlets—falling straightly to her white shoulders, comes forth from her cavern in the woods, and speaks to us in a low soft tone, that awes and wins our hearts, and looks to us with eyes whose steady light and supernatural brightness bewilder our soul.

Yes, whenever I hear the word—Wissahikon—I fancy its woods and waves, embodied in the form of an Indian Prophetess, of the far gone time.

Oh, there are strange legends hovering around these wild rocks and dells—legends of those Monks who dwelt there long ago, and worshipped God *without a creed*—legends of that far gone time, when the white robed Indian priests came up the dell at dead of night, leading the victim to the altar—to the altar of bloody sacrifice—that victim a beautiful and trembling girl.

Now let us listen to the Prophetess as she speaks, and while her voice thrills, her eyes fire us, let us hear from her lips the Legends of the olden times.

The Consecration of the Deliverer

It stood in the shadows of the Wissahikon woods, that ancient Monastery,* its dark walls canopied by the boughs of the gloomy pine, interwoven with leaves of grand old oaks.

From the waters of the wood-hidden stream, a winding road led up to its gates; a winding road overgrown with tall rank grass, and sheltered from the light by the thick branches above.

A Monastery? Yes, a Monastery, here amid the wilds of Wissahikon, in the year of Grace 1773, a Monastery built upon the soul of William Penn!

Let me paint it for you, at the close of this calm summer day.

The beams of the sun, declining far in the west, shoot between the thickly gathered leaves, and light up the green sward, around those massive gates, and stream with sudden glory over the dark walls. It is a Monastery, yet here we behold no swelling dome, no Gothic turrets, no walls of massive stone. A hugh edifice, built one hundred years ago of the trunks of giant oaks and pines, it rises amid the woods, like the temple of some long forgotten religion. The roof is broken into many fantastic forms—here it rises in a steep gable, yonder the heavy logs are laid prostrate; again they swell into a shapeless mass, as though stricken by a hurricane.

Not many windows are there in the dark old walls, but to the west four large square spaces framed in heavy pieces of timber, break on your eyes, while on the other sides of the old house one

---

* This building must not be confused with the historic Monastery built by the Zionistic Brotherhood in 1737. This was the ruin of what was once a block-house, a fort of defense in the earlier days.

blank mass of logs, rising on logs.

No: not one black mass, for at this time of the year, when the breath of June hides the Wissahikon in a world of leaves, the old Monastery looks like a grim soldier, who, scathed by time and battle, wears yet thick wreaths of laurel over his armour, and about his brow.

Green vines girdle the ancient house on every side. From the squares of the dark windows, from the intervals of the massive logs, they hang in luxuriant festoons, while the shapeless roof is all one mass of leaves.

Nay, even the wall of logs which extends around the old house, with a ponderous gate to the west, is green with the touch of June. Not a trunk but blooms with some drooping vine; even the gate posts, each a solid column of oak, seem to wave to and fro, as the summer breeze plays with their drapery of green leaves.

It is a sad, still hour. The beams of the sun stream with fitful splendor over the green sward. That strange old mansion seems as sad and desolate as the tomb. But suddenly—hark! Do you hear the clanking of those bolts, the crashing of the unclosing gates?

The gates creak slowly aside!—let us steal behind this cluster of pines, and gaze upon the inhabitants of the Monastery, as they come forth for their evening walk.

Three figures issue from the opened gates, an old man whose withered features and white hair are thrown strongly into the fading light, by his long robe of dark velvet. On one arm, leans a young girl, also dressed in black, her golden hair falling—not in ringlets—but in rich masses, to her shoulders. She bends upon his arm, and with that living smile upon her lips, and in her eyes, looks up into his face.

On the other arm, a young man, whose form, swelling with the proud outlines of early manhood, is attired in a robe or gown, dark as his father's while his bronzed face, shaded by curling brown hair, seems to reflect the silent thought, written upon the old man's brow.

They pace slowly along the sod. Not a word is spoken. The old man raises his eyes, and lifts the square cap from his brow— look! how that golden beam plays along his brow, while the evening breeze tosses his white hairs. There is much suffering, many deep traces of the Past, written on his wrinkled face, but the light of a wild enthusiasm beams from his blue eyes.

The young man—his dark eyes wildly glaring fixed upon the sod—moves by the old man's side, but speaks no word.

The girl, that image of maidenly grace, nurtured into beauty, within an hour's journey of the city, and yet afar from the world, still bends over the aged arm, and looks smilingly into that withered face, her glossy hair waving in the summer wind.

Who are these, that come hither, pacing, at the evening hour, along the wild moss? The father and his children!

What means that deep strange light, flashing not only from the blue eyes of the father, but from the dark eyes of his son?

Does it need a second glance to tell you, that it is the light of Fanaticism, that distortion of Faith, the wild glare of Superstition, that deformity of Religion?

The night comes slowly down. Still the Father and son pace the ground in silence, while the breeze freshens and makes low music among the leaves. Still the young girl, bending over the old man's arm, smiles tenderly in his face, as though she would drive the sadness from his brow with one gleam of her mild blue eyes.

At last—within the shadows of the gate, their faces lighted by the last gleam of the setting sun—the old man and his son stand like figures of stone, while each grasps a hand of the young girl.

Is it not a strange yet beautiful picture? The old Monastery forms one dense mass of shade; on either side extends the darkening forest, yet here, within the portals of the gate, the three figures are grouped, while a warm, soft mass of tufted moss, spreads before them. The proud manhood of the son, contrasted with the white locks of the father, the tender yet voluptuous beauty of the girl relieving the thought and sadness, which glooms over each brow.

Hold—the Father presses the wrist of the Son with a convulsive grasp—hush! Do you hear that low deep whisper?

"At last, it comes to my soul, the Fulfilment of the Prophecy!" he whispers and is silent again, but his lip trembles and his eyes glares.

"But the time—Father—*the time?*" the Son replies in the same deep voice, while his eyes, dilating, fire with the same feeling that swells his Father's heart.

"*The last day of this year—the third hour after midnight*—THE DELIVERER WILL COME!"

These words may seem lame and meaningless, when spoken again, but had you seen the look that kindled over the old man's face, his white hand raised above his head, had you heard his deep voice swelling through the silence of the woods, each word would ring on your ear, as though it quivered from a spirit's tongue.

Then the old man and his son knelt on the sod, while the young girl—looking in their faces with wonder and awe—sank silently besides them.

The tones of Prayer broke upon the stillness of the darkening woods.

Tell us the meaning of this scene. Wherefore call this huge edifice, where dark logs are clothed in green leaves, by the old world name of Monastery? Who are these—father, son and daughter—that dwell within its walls?

Seventeen years ago—from the year of Grace, 1773 *—there came to the wilds of the Wissahikon, a man in the prime of mature manhood, clad in a long, dark robe, with a cross of silver gleaming on his breast. With one arm he gathered to his heart a smiling babe, a little girl, whose golden hair floated over her dark dress like sunshine over a pall; by the hand he led a dark haired boy.

His name, his origin, his object in the wilderness, no one knew, but purchasing the ruined Block-House, which bore on its walls and timbers the marks of many an Indian fight, he shut himself out from all the world. His son, his daughter, grew up together in this wild solitude. The voice of prayer was often heard at dead of night, by the belated huntsman, swelling from the silence of the· lonely house.

By slow degrees, whether from the cross which the old stranger wore upon his breast, or from the sculptured images which had been seen within the walls of his forest home, the place was called—the Monastery—and its occupant the Priest.

Had he been drawn from his native home by crime? Was his name enrolled among the titled and the great of his Father-land, Germany? Or, perchance, he was one of those stern visionaries, the Pietists of Germany, who lashed alike by Catholic and Protestant persecutors, brought to the wilds of the Wissahikon their beautiful Fanaticism?

For that Fanaticism, professed by a band of brothers, who years before driven from Germany, came here to Wissahikon, built their Monastery, and worshipped God, without a written creed, was beautiful.

It was a wild belief, tinctured with the dreams of Alchemists, it

---

* The year 1860. One hundred years later, in fulfilment of the predictions of the founder of the Rosy Cross, Dr. P. B. Randolph, having been made Supreme Grand Master at Paris, founded the first Grand Lodge of the Rosy Cross under American Soil. Theretofore, only the Supreme Council of the Seven had convened in conclave, then the fulfilment of the promise, and America became the home of the august Fraternity.

may be, yet still full of faith in God, and love to man. Persecuted by the Protestants of Germany, as it was by the Catholics of France, it still treasured the Bible as its rule and the Cross as its symbol.

The Monastery, in which the brothers of the faith lived for long years * was situated on the brow of a hill, not a mile from the old Block-House. Here the Brothers had dwelt, in the deep serenity of their own hearts, until one evening they gathered in their garden, around the form of their dying father, who yielded his soul to God in their midst, while the setting sun and the calm silence of universal nature gave a strange grandeur to the scene.

But it was *not with this Brotherhood* that the stranger of the Block-House held communion.

His communion was with the dark-eyed son, who grew up, drinking the fanaticism of his father, in many a midnight watch with the golden-haired daughter, whose smile was wont to drive the gloom from his brow, the wearing anxiety from his heart.

Who was the stranger! No one knew. The farmer of the Wissahikon had often seen his dark-robed form passing like a ghost under the solemn pines; the wandering huntsman had many a time, on his midnight ramble, heard the sound of prayer breaking along the silence of the woods from the Block-House: yet still the life, origin, objects of the stranger were wrapt in impenetrable mystery.

Would you know more of his life? Would you penetrate the mystery of his dim old Monastery, shadowed by the thickly-clustered oaks and pines, shut out from the world by the barrier of impenetrable forests?

Would you know the meaning of those strange words, uttered by the old man, on the calm summer evening?

Come with me, then—at midnight—on the last day of 1773. We will enter the Block-House together, and behold a scene, which, derived from a tradition of the past, is well calculated to thrill the heart with a deep awe.

It is midnight: there is snow on the ground: the leafless trees fling their bared limbs against the cold blue of the starlit sky.

The old Block-House rises dark and gloomy from the snow, with

---

* This was the real Monastery of the Wissahikon. It was built 1737 by the Zionitic Brotherhood. The Zionitic Brotherhood was an Off-spring of the Seventh Day or German Baptists of Ephrata, an early Pietist Colony. The Baptists were merely one of the many Sectarians who left Germany, France and even Switzerland for America and Freedom. Rosicrucians were never persecuted as a class *because they were not known to the multitude.*

the heavy trees extending all around.

The wind sweeps through the woods, not with a boisterous roar, but the strange sad cadence of an organ, whose notes swell away through the arches of a dim cathedral aisle.

Who would dream that living beings tenanted this dark mansion, arising in one black mass from the bed of snow, its huge timbers, revealed in various indistinct forms, by the cold clear light of the stars? Centred in the midst of the desolate woods, it looks like the abode of spirits, or yet like some strange sepulchre, in which the dead of long-past ages lie entombed.

There is no foot-track on the winding road—the snow presents one smooth white surface—yet the gates are thrown wide open, as if ready for the coming of a welcome guest.

Through this low, narrow door—also flung wide open—along this dark corridor, we will enter the Monastery.

In the centre of this room, illuminated by the light of two tall white candles sits the old man, his slender form clad in dark velvet, with the silver cross gleaming on his bosom, buried in the cushions of an oaken chair.

His slender hands are laid upon his knees—he sways slowly to and fro—while his large blue eye, dilating with a wild stare, is fixed upon the opposite wall.

Hush! Not a word—not even the creaking of a footstep—for this old man, wrapped in his thoughts, sitting alone in the centre of this strangely furnished room, fills us with involuntary reverence.

Strangely furnished room? Yes, circular in form, with a single doorway, huge panels of dark oaken wainscot, rise from the bared floor to the gloomy ceiling. Near the old man arises a white altar, on which the candles are placed, its spotless curtain floating down to the floor. Between the candles, you behold, a long, slender flagon of silver, a wreath of laurel leaves, fresh gathered from the Wissahikon hills, and a Holy Bible, bound in velvet, with antique clasps of gold.

Behind the altar, gloomy and sullen, as if struggling with the shadows of the room, arises a cross of Iron.

On yonder small fire-place, rude logs of oak and hickory send up their mingled smoke and flame.

The old man sits there, his eyes growing wilder in their gaze every moment, fixed upon the solitary door. Still he sways to and fro, and now his thin lips move, and a faint murmur fills the room.

"*He will come!*" mutters the Priest of the Wissahikon, as common rumor named him. "*At the third hour after midnight, the De-*

liverer will come!"

These words acquire a singular interest from the tone and look which accompany their utterance.

Hark—the door opens—the young man with the bronzed face and deep dark eyes, appears—advances to his father's side.

"Father"—whispers the young man—"May it not be a vain fancy after all! This hope that the Deliverer will come ere the rising of the sun?"

You can see the old man turn suddenly round—his eye blazes as he grasps his son by the wrist.

"Seventeen years ago, I left my father-land, became an exile and an outcast! Seventeen years ago I forsook the towers of my race, that even now, darken over the bosom of the Rhine—I, whose name was ennobled by the ancestral glories of thirteen centuries, turned my back at once on pomp, power—all that is worshipped by the herd of mankind! In my native land they have believed me dead for many years—the castle, the broad domains that by the world's law, my son, now own another's rule—and here we are, side by side, in this rude temple of the Wissahikon! Why is this, my son? Speak, Paul, and answer me, why do we dwell together, the father and his children, in this wild forest of a strange land?"

The son veiled his eyes with his clasped hands: the emotion of his father's look, thrilled him to the soul.

"I will tell you why! Seventeen years ago, as I bent over the body of my dead wife, even in the death-vault of our castle, on the Rhine, the voice of God, spake to my soul—bade me resign the world and its toys—bade me take my children and go forth to a strange land!"

"And there await the Fulfilment of Prophecy!" whispered Paul, raising his head from his clasped hands.

"For seventeen years I have buried my soul in the pages of that book"—

"I have shared your studies, father! Reared afar from the toil and the vanity of worldly life, I have made my home with you in this hermitage. Together we have wept—prayed—watched over the pages of Revelation!"

"You have become part of my soul," said the Priest of Wissahikon, in a softened voice, as he laid his withered hand upon the white forehead of his son: "You might have been noble in your native land; yes, your sword might have carved for you a gory renown from the corpses of dead men, butchered in battle; or the triumphs of poetry and art, might have clothed your brow in laurel, and yet you have chosen your lot with me; with me devoted life and soul to the perusal of God's solemn book!"

The dark eye of the son began to burn, with the same wild light that blazed over his father's face.

"And our studies, our long and painful search into the awful world, which the Bible opens to our view, has ended in a knowledge of these great truths—*The Old World is sunk in all manner of crime, as was the Ante-Diluvian World;*—THE NEW WORLD *is given to man as a refuge, even as the Ark was given to Noah and his children.*

"*The New World is the last altar of human freedom left on the surface of the Globe. Never shall the footsteps of Kings pollute its soil. It is the last hope of man.* God has spoken, and it is so.—Amen!"

The old man's voice rang, in deep, solemn tones, through the lonely room, while his eye seemed to burn as with the fire of Prophecy.

"The voice of God has spoken to me, in my thoughts by the day, in my dreams by night—*I will send a* DELIVERER *to this land of the New World, who shall save my people from physical bondage, even as my Son saved them from the bondage of spiritual death!*

"And tonight he will come, at the third hour after midnight, he will come through yonder door, and take upon himself his great Mission, to free the New World from the yoke of the Tyrant!

"Yes, my son, six months ago, on that calm summer evening, as with Catherine leaning on one arm, you on the other, I strolled forth along the woods, that voice whispered a message to my soul! Tonight the Deliverer will come!"

"All is ready for his coming!" exclaimed Paul, advancing to the altar. "Behold the Crown, the Flagon of Anointing Oil, the Bible and the Cross!"

The old man arose, lifting his withered hands above his head, while the light streamed over his silver hairs.

"Even as the Prophets of old anointed the brows of men, chosen by God to do great deeds in His name, so will I—purified by the toil and prayer, and self-denial of seventeen long years—anoint the forehead of the Deliverer!"

Hark! As the voice of the aged enthusiast, tremulous with emotion, quivers on the air, the clock in the hall without, tells the hour of twelve! As the tones of that bell ring through the lonely Block House, like a voice from the other world—deep, sad and echoing— the last minute of 1773 sank in the glass of Time, and 1774 was born.

Then they knelt, silently beside the altar, the old man and his son. The white hair of the Priest, mingled with the brown locks of Paul; their hands clasped together rested upon the Bible, which was opened at the Book of Revelations.

Their separate prayers breathed in low whispers from each lip, mingled together, and went up to Heaven in ONE.

An hour passed. Hark! Do you hear the old clock again? How that sullen ONE! swells through the silent halls!

Still they kneel together there—still the voice of prayer quivers from each tongue.

Another hour, spent in silent prayer, with bowed head and bended knees. As the clock speaks out the hour of two, the old man rises and paces the floor.

"Place your hand upon my heart, my son! Can you feel its throbbings? Upon my brow—ah! it burns like living fire! The hour draws nigh—he come! Yes, my heart throbs, my brain fires, but my faith in God is firm—the Deliverer will come!"

Vain were the attempt to picture the silent agony of that old man's face! Call him dreamer—call him fanatic—what you will, you must still admit that a great soul throbbed within his brain— still you must reverence the strong heart which beats within his shrunken chest.

Still must you remember that this old man was once a renowned lord; that he forsook all that the world holds dear, buried himself for seventeen years in the wilds of this forest, his days and nights spent amid the dark pages of the Revelations of Saint John.

Up and down the oaken floor, now by the altar, where the light shone over his brow, now in the darkness where the writhings of his countenance were lost in the shadows, the old man hurried along, his eye blazing with a wilder light, his withered cheek with a warmer glow.

Meanwhile the son remained kneeling in prayer. The lights burned dimly—the room was covered with a twilight gloom. Still the Iron Cross was seen—the whole altar still broke through the darkness, with its silver Flagon and Laurel Crown.

Hark! That sound—the clock is on the hour of three! The old man starts, quivers, listens!

ONE! rings through the desolate mansion.

"I hear no sound!" mutters the enthusiast. But the words had not passed his lips, when TWO! swells on the air.

"He comes not!" cries Paul, darting to his feet, his features quivering with suspense. They clasp their hands together—they listen with frenzied intensity.

"Still no footsteps! Not a sound!" gasps Paul.

"But he *will* come!" and the old man, sublime in the energy of fanaticism, towered erect, one hand to his heart, while the other quivered in the air.

THREE! The last stroke of the bell swelled—echoed—and died away.

"He comes not!" gasped the son, in agony. "But yes! Is there not a footstep on the frozen snow? Hark! Father, father! do you hear that footstep? It is on the threshold now—it advances—"

"He comes!" whispers the old man, while the sweat stood out in beads from his withered brow.

—"It advances, father! Yes, along the hall—hark! There is a hand on the door—hah! It is but a delusion—no! He is come at last!"

"At last he is come!" gasped the old man, and with one impulse they sank on their knees. Hark! You hear the old door creak on its hinges, as it swings slowly open—a strange voice breaks the silence.

"Friends, I have lost my way in the forest," said the voice, speaking in a calm, manly voice. "Can you direct me to the right way?"

The old man looked up; a cry of wonder trembled from his lips. As for the son, he gazed in silence on the Stranger, while his features were stamped with inexpressible surprise.

The Stranger stood on the threshold, his face to the light, his form thrown boldly forward, by the darkness at his back.

He stood there, not as a Conqueror on the battlefield, with the spoils of many nations trampled under his feet.

Towering above the stature of common men, his form was clad in the dress of a plain gentleman of his time, fashioned of black velvet, with ruffles on the bosom and around the wrist, diamond buckles gleaming from his shoes.

Broad in the shoulders, beautiful in the sinewy proportions of each limb, he stood there, extending his hat in one hand, while the other gathered his heavy cloak around the arm.

His white forehead, large, overarched eyes, which gleamed even through the darkness of the room with a calm, clear light; his lips were firm; his chin round and full; the general contour of his face stamped with the settled beauty of mature manhood, mingled with the fire of chivalry.

In one word, he was a man whom you would single out among a

crowd of ten thousand, for his grandeur of bearing, his calm, collected dignity of expression and manner.

"Friends," he again began, as he started back, surprised at the sight of the kneeling enthusiasts, "I have lost my way—"

"Thou hast not lost thy way," spoke the voice of the old man, as he arose and confronted the Stranger; "thou hast found thy way to usefulness and immortal renown!"

The Stranger advanced a footstep, while a warm glow overspread his commanding face. Paul stood as if spellbound by the calm gaze of his clear, deep eyes.

"Nay—do not start, nor gaze upon me in such wonder! I tell thee the voice that speaks from my lips, is the voice of Revelation. Thou art called to a great work; kneel before the altar and receive thy mission!"

Nearer to the altar drew the Stranger.

"This is but folly—you make a mock of men!" he began; but the wild gaze of the old man thrilled his heart, as with magnetic fire. He paused, and stood silent and wondering.

"Nay, doubt me not! Tonight, filled with strange thoughts on your country's Future, you laid yourself down to sleep within your habitation in yonder city. But sleep fled from your eyes—a feeling of restlessness drove you forth into the cold air of night—"

"This is true!" muttered the Stranger in a musing voice, while his face expressed surprise.

"As you dashed along, mounted on the steed which soon will bear your form in the ranks of battle, the cold air of the night fanned your hot brow, but could not drive from your soul the Thought of your Country!"

"How knew you this?" and the Stranger started forward, grasping the old man suddenly by the wrist.

Deeper and bolder thrilled the tones of the old Enthusiast.

"The rein fell loosely on your horse's neck—you let him wander, you cared not whither! Still the thought that oppressed your soul was the future of your country. Still great hopes—dim visions of *what is to come*—floating panoramas of battle and armed legions—darted one by one over your soul. Even as you stood on the threshold of yonder door, asking, in calm tones, the way through the forest, another and deeper question rose to your lips—

"I confess it!" said the Stranger, his tone catching the deep emotion of the old man's voice. "As I stood upon the threshold, the question that rose to my lips was—

"Is it lawful for a SUBJECT *to draw sword against his* KING?"

71

"Man! You read the heart!" and this strange man of commanding form and thoughtful brow, gazed fixedly in the eyes of the Enthusiast, while his face expressed every conflicting emotion of doubt, suspicion, surprise and awe.

"Nay, do not gaze upon me in such wonder! I tell thee a great work has been allotted unto thee, by the FATHER of all souls! Kneel by this altar—and here, in the silence of night, amid the depths of these wild woods—will I anoint thee Deliverer of this great land, even as the men of Judah, in the far-gone time, anointed the brows of the chosen David!"

It may have been a sudden impulse, or perchance, some conviction of the future flashed over the Stranger's soul, but as the gloom of that chamber gathered round him, as the voice of the old man thrilled in his ear, he felt those knees, which never yielded to man, sink beneath him, he bowed before the altar, his brow bared, laid his hands upon the Book of God.

The light flashed over his bold features, glowing with the beauty of manhood in its prime, over his proud form, dilating with a feeling of inexpressible agitation.

On one side of the altar stood the old man—The Priest of the Wissahikon—his silver hair waving aside from his flushed brow— on the other, his son, bronzed in face, but thoughtful in the steady gaze of his large eyes.

Around this strange group all was gloom: the cold wintry air poured through the open door, but they heeded it not.

"Thou art called to the great work of a Champion and Deliverer! Soon thou wilt ride to battle at the head of legions—soon thou wilt lead a people to freedom—soon thy sword will gleam like a meteor over the ranks of war!"

As the voice of the old man in the dark robe, with the silver cross flashing in his heart, thrills through the chamber—as the Stranger bows his head as if in reverence, while the dark-browed son looks silently on—look yonder in the dark shadows of the doorway!

A young form, with a dark mantle floating round her white robes, stands trembling there. As you look, her blue eye dilates with fear, her hair streams in a golden shower, down to the uncovered shoulders. Her finger is pressed against her lip; she stands doubting, fearing, trembling on the threshold.

Unseen by all, she fears that her father may work harm to the kneeling Stranger. What knows she of his wild dreams of enthusiasm? The picture which she beholds terrifies her. This small and gloomy chamber, lighted by the white candles—the altar rising in the gloom—the Iron Cross confronting the kneeling man, like a thing of evil omen—her brother, mute and wondering, her father, with white hairs floating aside from his flushed forehead. The picture was singular and impressive: the winter wind, moaning sullenly without, imparted a sad and organ-like music to the scene.

"Dost thou promise, that when the appointed time arrives, thou wilt be found ready, sword in hand, to fight for thy country and thy God?"

It was in tones broken by emotion, that the Stranger simply answered—"I do!"

"Dost thou promise, in the hour of thy glory—when a nation shall bow before thee—as in the fierce hour of adversity—when thou shalt behold thy soldiers starving for want of bread—to remember the great truth, written in these words—'*I am but the Minister of God in the great work of a nation's Freedom.*'"

Again the bowed head, again the tremulous—"I do promise!"

"Then, in His name, who gave the New World to the millions of the human race, as the last altar of their rights, I do consecrate thee its—DELIVERER!"

With the finger of his extended hand, touched with the anointing oil, he described the figure of a Cross on the white forehead of the Stranger, who raised his eyes, while his lips murmured as if in prayer.

Never was nobler King anointed beneath the shadow of Cathedral arch—never did holier Priest administer the solemn vow! A poor Cathedral, this rude Block House of the Wissahikon—a plainly-clad gentleman, this kneeling Stranger—a wild Enthusiast, the old man! I grant it all. And yet, had you seen the Enthusiasm of the white-haired Minister, reflected in the Stranger's brow, and cheek, and eyes, had you marked the contrast between the shrunken form of the "Priest," and the proud figure of the Anointed—both quivering with the same agitation—you would confess with me, that this Consecration was full as holy, in the sight of Heaven, as that of "Good King George."

And all the while that young man stood gazing on the Stranger in silent awe, while the girl, trembling on the threshold, a warm glow lightens up her face, as she beheld the scene.

"When the time comes, go forth to victory! On thy brow, no conqueror's blood-red wreath, but this crown of fadeless laurel!"

He extends his hand, as if to wreathe the Stranger's brow, with the leafy crown—yet look! A young form steals up to his side, seizes the crown from his hand, and, ere you can look again, it falls upon the bared brow of the kneeling man.

He looks up and beholds that young girl, with the dark mantle gathered over her white robes, stands blushing and trembling before the altar, as though frightened at the boldness of the deed.

"It is well!" said the aged man, regarding his daughter with a kindly smile. "From whom should the Deliverer of a Nation receive his crown of laurel, but from the hands of a stainless woman!"

"Rise! The Champion and Leader of a People!" spoke the deep voice of the son, as he stood before the altar, surveying, with one glance, the face of his father—the countenance of the blushing girl, and the bowed head of the Stranger. "Rise, sir, and take this hand, which was never yet given to man! I know not your name, yet, on this book, I swear to be faithful to thee, even to the death!"

The Stranger rose, proudly he stood there, as with the consciousness of his commanding look and form. The laurel-wreath encircled his white forehead; the cross, formed by the anointing oil, glistened in the light.

Paul, the son, buckled a sword to his side; the old man extended his hands as if in blessing, while the young girl looked up silently into his face.

They all beheld the form of this strange man shake with emotion; while that face, whose calm beauty had won their hearts, now quivered in every fibre.

The wind moaned sadly over the frozen snow, yet these words, uttered by the Stranger, were heard distinctly by all—

"From you, old man, I take the vow! From you, fair girl, the laurel! From you, brave friend, the sword! On this book I swear to be faithful unto all!"

And as the light flashed over his quivering features, he laid his hand upon the Book and kissed the hilt of the sword.

Years passed.

The memory of that New Year's night of 1774, perchance, had passed with years, and lost all place in the memory of living being.

America was a nation—Washington was President.

Through the intervals of the trees shine the beams of the declining sun, but the Block House was a mass of ruins. Burned one night by the British, in the darkest hour of the war, its blackened timbers were yet encircled by green leaves.

Still the smiling sun shone over the soft sward and among the thickly clustered trees of Wissahikon.

But Father—Son—Daughter—where are they?

Yonder, a square enclosure of stone shuts three green mounds out from the world.

The sad story of their lives may not be told in few words. The terrors of that night when the Block House was fired, and—but we must not speak it! All we can say—look yonder, and behold their graves!

Hark! The sound of horses' hoofs! A man of noble presence appears, guiding his gallant grey steed, along the winding road. He dismounts; the horse wanders idly over the sod, cropping the fragrant wild grass.

This man of noble presence, dressed in plain black velvet, with a star gleaming on his breast, with a face, magnificent in its wrinkled age, as it was beautiful in its chivalric manhood—this man of noble presence, before whom Kings may stand uncovered, approaches the ruin of the Block House.

Do you see his eye light up again with youthful fire, his lip quiver with an agitation deeper than battle-rage?

There he stands, while the long shadows of the trees darken far over the sward—there, while the twilight deepens into night, gazing with a heaving chest and quivering lip, upon the ruins of the old Block House.

Perchance he thinks of the dead, or it may be his thoughts are with scenes of the Past—perchance, even now, a strange picture rises before him!

—That picture a darkened chamber, with a white altar rising in its centre, while an old man, and his brave son, and virgin daughter, all gather round a warrior form, hailing him with one voice—

"THE DELIVERER."

GEORGE WASHINGTON

Member, Great, or World Council, Fraternitas: The Deliverer

Commander in Chief of the American Army, first President of the United States of America, member of the *World*, or *Great Council,* not only an associate of George Clymer and LaFayette, but a personal friend of both.

George Washington was born in Westmoreland, Virginia, February 22, 1732.

Washington, like Napoleon, once a member of the *Great* or *World Council,* had an opportunity to prove false to his trust and become King of America, as Napoleon became Emperor of France, but Washington remained true to the trust imposed on him and fought for the freedom of the American people.

Washington, in spirit and religion, was a true *Unknown,* or *Inconnu.*

Because of his destiny as a leader of the people he was Immortalized by his works. If we say no more of him it is because all the world is familiar with his service to the people, even though his spiritual life has remained unknown to all but a very few.

ADDENDA

Basically, the work of the Fraternity of the Rosicrucians is to teach mankind the principles of a spiritual religion free from creed and dogma, based upon the Mystic and Occult sciences of the past and present ages. The Fraternity does not condemn formal religion and an aspirant is not encouraged to sever his former connection with religious institutions unless their teachings interfere with the Freedom of Man or oppose the Brotherhood of Man.

The Fraternity is forbidden by the rules established by the First Supreme Council either to proselyte or to advertise for members. Contact between aspirant and the Fraternity must be effected in an indirect manner. Those truly interested in the Work and Teachings of the Rosy Cross, and who seek detailed information concerning methods of instruction, may accomplish such contact by writing to the address here appended.

Primarily, the Fraternity teaches the laws which govern the welfare of Man, that every dormant faculty, both material and spiritual, may be developed to the fullest extent. Instruction and training is strictly individual. Things of the Soul belong only to the Soul and the Neophyte may make a confidant, in matters of Soul experience, only of the Master who is his teacher. The Soul must worship and grow in silence and the failure to observe this Law may prevent a Neophyte from attaining his goal. No one, whether Master or Neophyte, knows to what degree or grade an aspirant may attain nor the time that may be required in the instance of any individual to attain even the first degree. Members or students are not permitted to disclose either the name or meeting place of lodge or unit.

The Fraternity is strictly non-sectarian and the religion of the aspirant may not be questioned. Every man is admitted on a basis of equality. After admittance his fitness for advancement must be proven by himself. Those truly interested in the contents of this monograph may address Department of Instruction, Beverly Hall, Quakertown, Pennsylvania.

THE GREAT WORK

Throughout the pages of the present text the term THE GREAT WORK has been used time and again and many who will read the book and are not familiar with *Arcane* philosophy, instructions and guidance will question what this term applies to and includes.

The various terms used so frequently have a common objective in view: THE AWAKENING OF THE HIDDEN, LATENT SPIRITUAL SELF WITHIN MAN THAT BY BRINGING THIS ABOUT MAN MAY BECOME SPIRITUALLY CONSCIOUS, THE "GOD" SPOKEN OF BY ST. JOHN AND THE "SON OF GOD" MENTIONED BY THE FATHER OF MANKIND.

Those sufficiently interested may request a descriptive monograph.

Address: Department of Instructions
Beverly Hall Corporation
"Beverly Hall,"
Quakertown, Penna.
18951